How To Make Optical Illusion Tricks & Toys

E. Richard Churchill

Illustrated by James Michaels

For Sheila Anne Barry—with many thanks.

Special thanks to Sean, a chemical engineer who understands optical illusions.

Library of Congress Cataloging-in-Publication Data

Churchill, E. Richard (Elmer Richard)
How to make optical illusion tricks & toys.

Rev. ed. of: Optical illusion tricks & toys.
1989.
Summary: Presents more than sixty optical illusions that include tricks, drawings, and toys that can be assembled.
1. Optical illusions—Juvenile literature.
2. Educational toys—Juvenile literature.
[1. Optical illusions. 2. Toy making]
I. Churchill, E. Richard (Elmer Richard). Optical illusion tricks and toys, c1989. II. Title.
QP495.C48 1990 152.14′8 89-26169

ISBN 0-8069-6869-9 paper

3 5 7 9 10 8 6 4 2

Published by Sterling Publishing Company, Inc.
387 Park Avenue South, New York, N.Y. 10016
First published in hardcover under the title
Optical Illusion Tricks & Toys
Distributed in Canada by Sterling Publishing
% Canadian Manda Group, P.O. Box 920, Station U
Toronto, Ontario, Canada M8Z 5P9
Distributed in Great Britain and Europe by Cassell PLC
Artillery House, Artillery Row, London SW1P 1RT, England
Distributed in Australia by Capricorn Ltd.
P.O. Box 665, Lane Cove, NSW 2066
Manufactured in the United States of America

Contents

· 1 ·
Movers, Floaters, and Spotters

An optical illusion is something that looks different from what it really is. Some optical illusions, like the ones in this book, look different because they seem to move.

Some optical illusions appear because we have two eyes, while others are the result of our brain remembering one thing while our eyes are seeing another. Still other illusions happen because we think we see one thing when we actually see something else.

Here are a few optical illusions that result from seeing things with two eyes.

The Floating Finger

Hold your two hands in front of your face at eye level, about 15 inches away from your eyes. Illus. 1 shows how. Keep the tips of your index fingers about 1 inch apart.

Illus. 1

Focus on a wall several feet behind your fingers. Almost at once you will see something strange. Between the tips of your fingers is a tiny, disembodied finger floating in space. Strangest of all is the fact that this little finger has two tips, one at either end.

Slowly move your hands closer to your face. Keep the tips of your fingers the same distance apart. The nearer your hands come to your face the longer the little floating finger becomes.

Pull your hands away from your face and the little two-ended finger gets shorter and shorter. Illus. 2 shows this illusion.

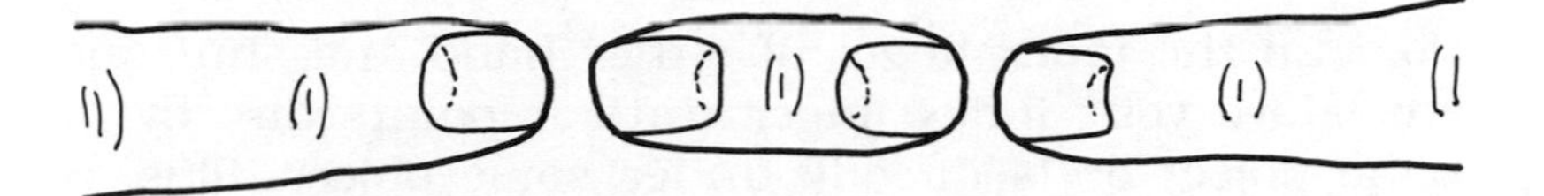

Illus. 2

Now, focus your eyes on your fingers instead of the wall. Just like that, the floating finger vanishes.

When your fingers move closer to your face the space between them enters a "blind spot" (you'll find out more about these on page 13). Rather than go blind, your brain knows what should be there and fills the spot with what your eyes *do* see. In this case, your eyes see the ends of your fingers and your brain uses this sight to fill the blind spot. That's why you see the floating finger even though it's not there, and why it disappears when you look at your actual fingers.

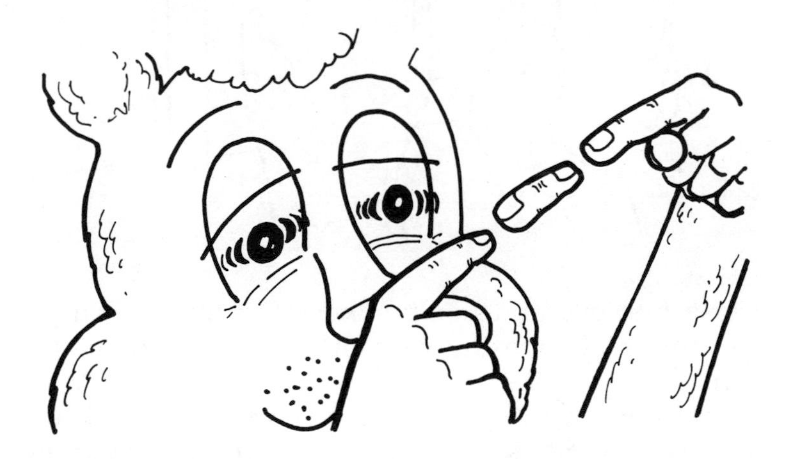

The Jumping Finger

Hold up the index finger of either hand and shut one eye. Move your index finger until it points directly at some object or is directly under some object. Illus. 3 shows how.

Illus. 3

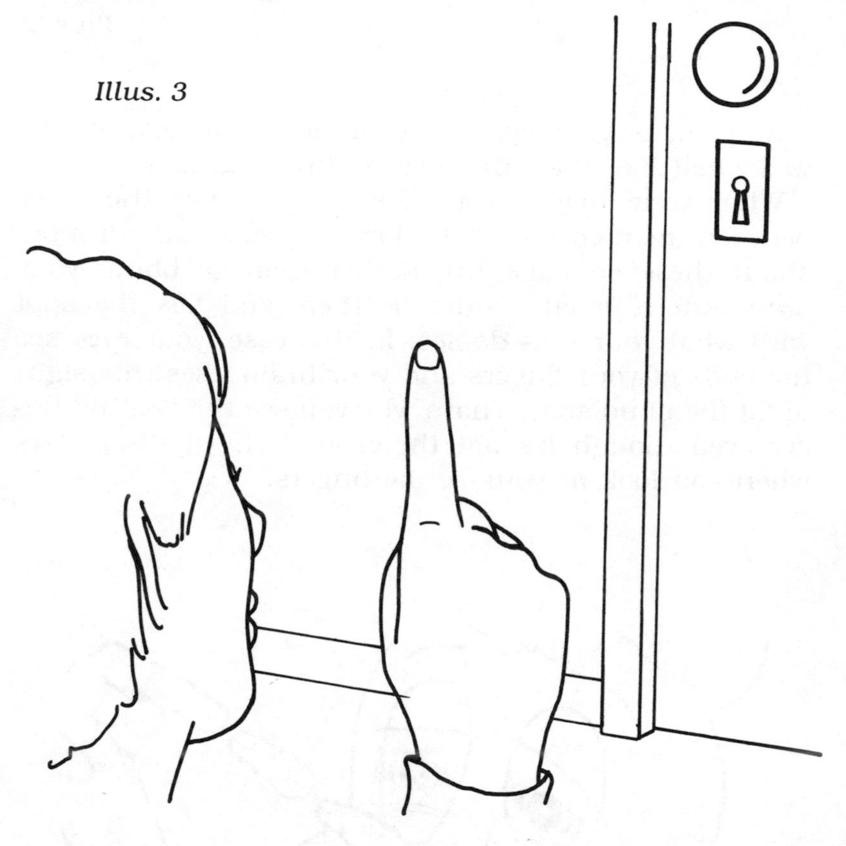

Close one eye and don't move your finger. Did your finger jump? Try closing your other eye. It jumped back again!

Of course your finger did not move (at least it's not supposed to). So what happened? Because your eyes are several inches apart, each one actually sees a slightly different picture. Your brain puts the two pictures together to tell how far an object is.

The Bouncing Ring

Open up both your eyes and form your thumb and forefinger into a ring like the one in Illus. 4.

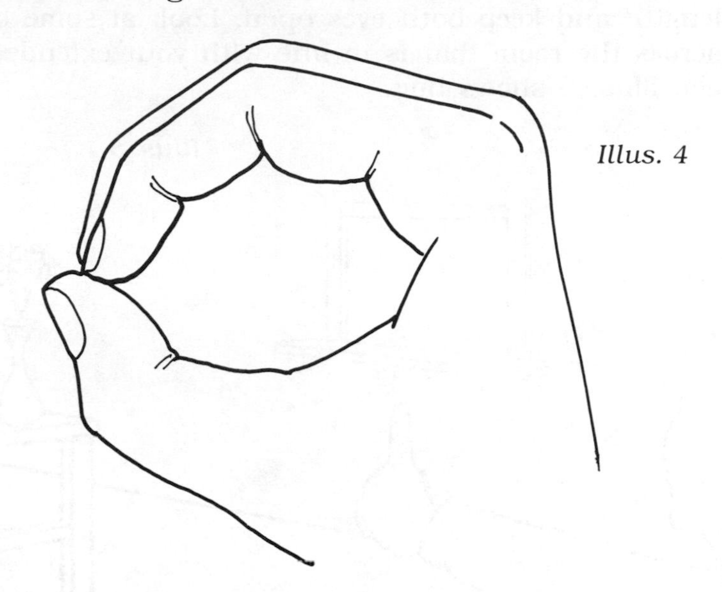

Illus. 4

Hold this ring out at arm's length. Move it around until you find something across the room which fits nicely into the ring. Focus your eyes on the object inside the ring.

Close one eye. Is the object still inside the ring? Depending on which eye you closed, the ring may stay still or bounce back.

Without moving your ring, close your open eye and open your closed eye. Now what do you see inside your ring?

With one eye open the object lines up inside the ring, but with your other eye open the object bounces away. Why?

When you see things with both eyes one eye has more control than the other. The eye that has more control is sometimes called the "dominant eye." When you close your dominant eye, the picture changes.

Growing New Fingers

While you're holding hands and fingers up, here's another moving illusion. Hold your index finger at arm's length, and keep both eyes open. Look at some object across the room that is in line with your extended finger. Illus. 5 shows how.

Illus. 5

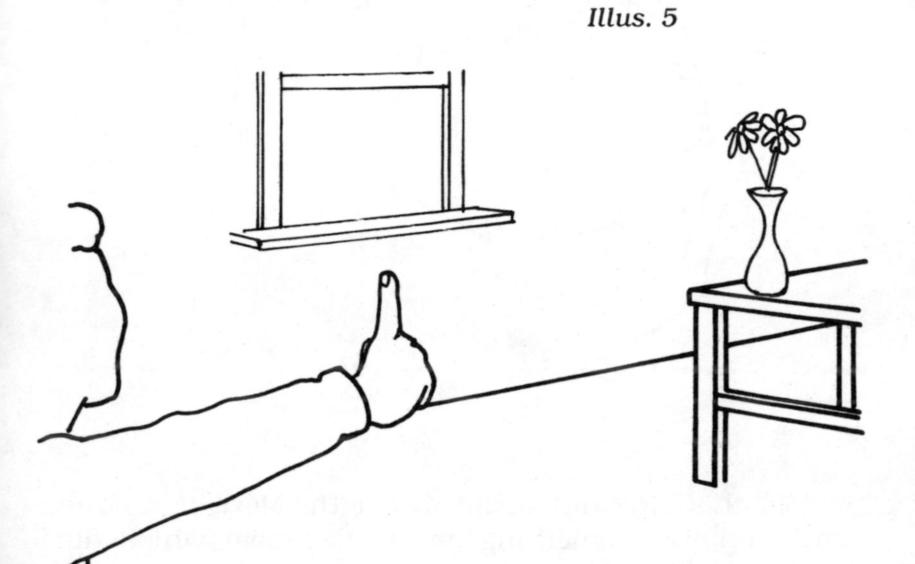

Focus on the object across the room and now you've got an extra finger.

Now focus on your finger. You see *two* objects instead of one!

Obviously, you did not suddenly grow an extra finger, nor did the object across the room suddenly double. What you did was see two different pictures with each eye.

Blind Spots

Do we always see—all the time—unless our eyes are closed or we are in a dark place? Maybe, maybe not.

Hold Illus. 6 about 15 inches in front of your face. Close your left eye, and look directly at the airplane with your right (open) eye.

Illus. 6

Slowly move the book closer to you, looking *directly* at the airplane with your right eye. Move the book closer and farther until something strange happens. Suddenly the rocket will disappear!

No, it didn't leap off the page, or move somewhere else. What happened was it got lost in your blind spot. Don't worry, everyone has one in each eye, so you're not going blind.

Now close your right eye and open your left. With the left eye stare directly at the rocket, and move the illustration closer and farther until suddenly the airplane disappears. The plane moved into the blind spot in your left eye.

Viewing the illustration with only one eye at a time you get a chance to locate your blind spot. When you are looking at things with both eyes this tiny blind spot causes no problem. What one eye does not see the other does.

Hole in Your Hand

Do you have a hole in the palm of your hand? No? Don't be too sure.

Roll a sheet of notebook paper into a hollow tube about 1 inch across. Hold the tube to keep it from unrolling or use a strip of cellophane tape to fasten the loose edge down. This is up to you.

Hold the tube up to one eye as in Illus. 7. Keep your other eye open.

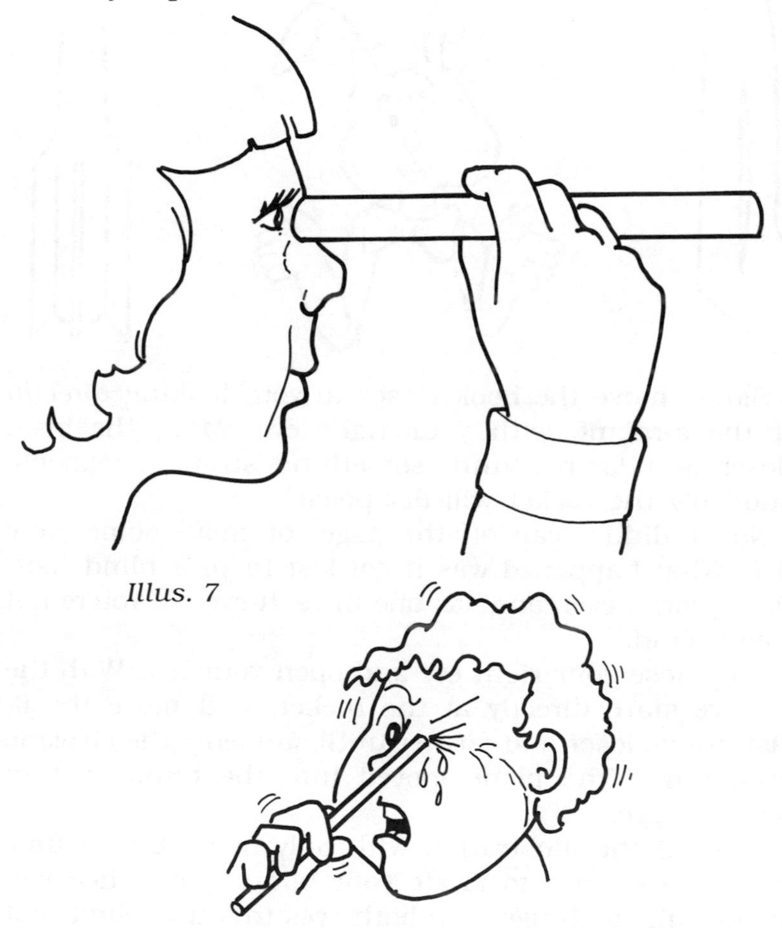

Illus. 7

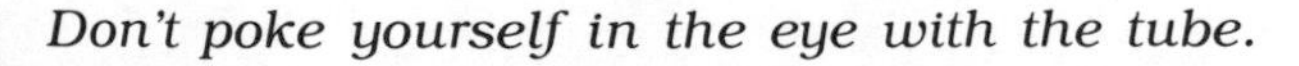

Don't poke yourself in the eye with the tube.

Locate something across the room that is small enough to be seen through the hollow tube. The object should be 12 or 15 fcct away. Kccp both eycs open, and look at the object through the tube.

Now bring your other hand up in front of the eye not looking through the paper tube. (Illus. 8 shows how to do this.) Suddenly you develop a round hole in the palm of your hand! And you're looking at the object through that round hole!

Illus. 8

Naturally, this is just an optical illusion. This is one more time when seeing with both eyes makes you think things are not as they actually are.

Now is as good a time as any to mention the fact that you will get lots more fun out of this book when you share the illusions with others. See how each moving optical illusion works. Then share it with friends and family.

The Travelling Rectangle

Sometimes your brain remembers an image even after you no longer see it. This is another optical illusion that moves from place to place.

Stare directly at the black rectangle in Illus. 9. Count to 30 as you stare. Try to blink as little as possible, but don't worry if a blink or two slips in. It won't spoil anything.

Illus. 9

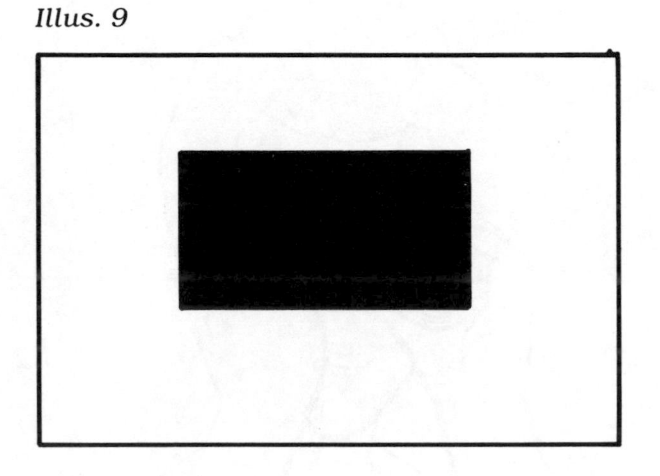

After staring for a count of 30, look up from the page. Now stare right at a dark wall or some other dark surface. Keep staring. What appears?

You know the rectangle didn't move off the page, but there it is! Even stranger than the fact that the rectangle moved to the wall is the fact that the one on the wall is light or even white instead of black like the one in the book!

This is called *afterimage*. Afterimage is responsible for many moving optical illusions. Some of them trick us into thinking we see colors that are different from those we really see. But more about that later.

Lines and Lines

Take a quick look at Illus. 10. As you can see there are two slanting lines that meet two parallel lines.

Illus. 10

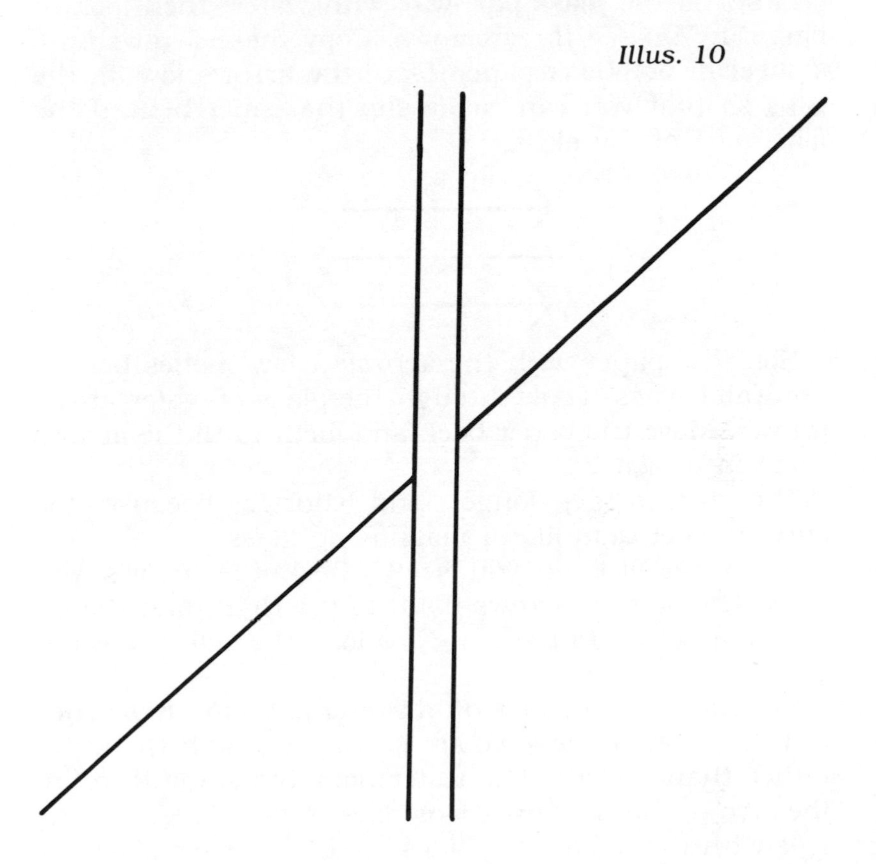

So what is so special about this? The special thing is that your eyes and mind have created an optical illusion.

Let's see if a little moving around will clear up the illusion. Take a piece of paper with a straight edge. Place the straight edge along the two slanted lines.

This is one of those times when just a little movement does an amazing thing to an optical illusion.

Three Arrows

For this illusion you need a glass that you can see through.

First, fill the glass part-way with water; then look at Illus. 11. You see three arrows. Copy these arrows onto a sheet of notebook paper. Place the arrows low on the page so that you can easily slip the paper behind the filled part of the glass.

Illus. 11

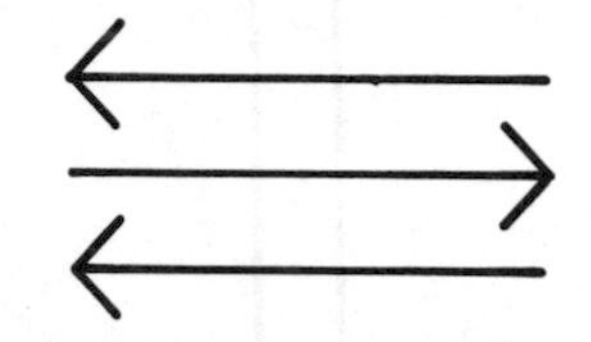

Hold the paper with the arrows a few inches behind the water glass. Look through the glass of water at the arrows. Move the paper back and forth until the arrows come into focus.

The arrows get longer and shorter, because the curved water acts like a magnifying glass.

But what else do you see? Check the arrows you drew. The outside arrows point to the right, and the inside one points to the left. Now look through the water again.

Of course, the arrows didn't reverse themselves. They look this way because you're looking through the water rather than the air. The water does the same thing to the arrows that a convex lens does. A convex lens is the type with the bulged-out sides, and it reverses whatever you're looking at. Illus. 12 shows how the light enters the glass of water, and how it reaches your eye.

Illus. 12

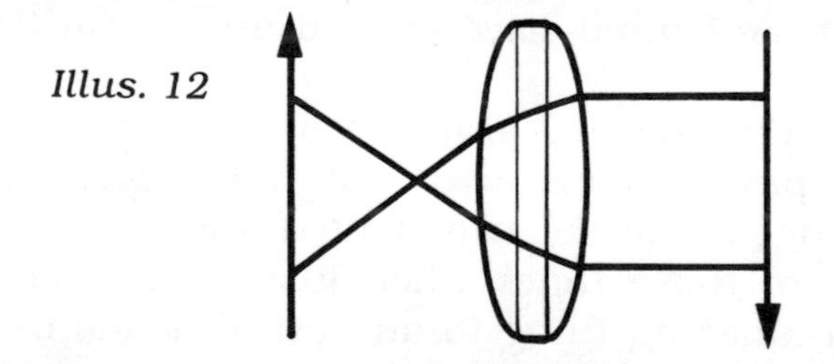

The Broken Pencil

While you have the water glass handy, find a pencil. Holding the pencil vertically, dip the point into the water.

Move either your head or the glass so that your eyes are directly in line with the surface of the water. Illus. 13 shows what you'll see. Once again, the "convex" water has bent the light, and the pencil in it.

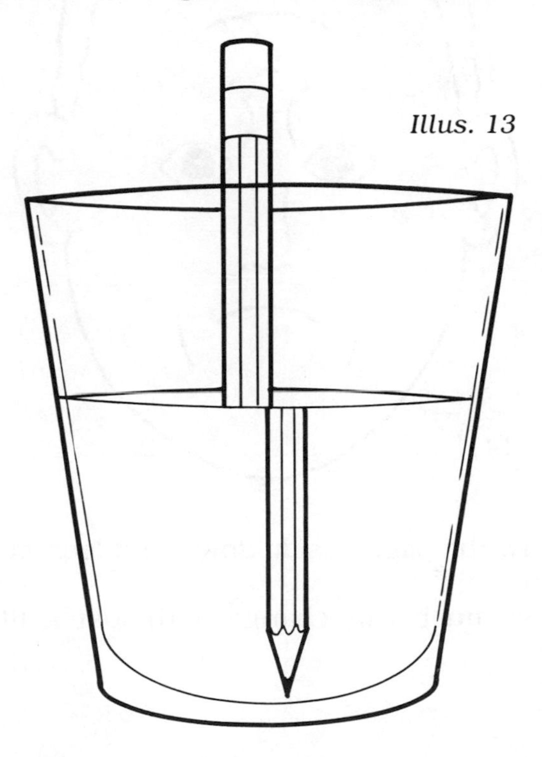

Illus. 13

Tip the pencil a little from side to side. Lift it up in the water just a bit.

Many years ago a state had a law that was based on this sort of optical illusion. The law said that a person who saw a crime committed on the other side of a glass window could not be a witness, because glass was convex and poorly made in those days. The glass created the illusion.

Two-Faced

Look at Illus. 14.

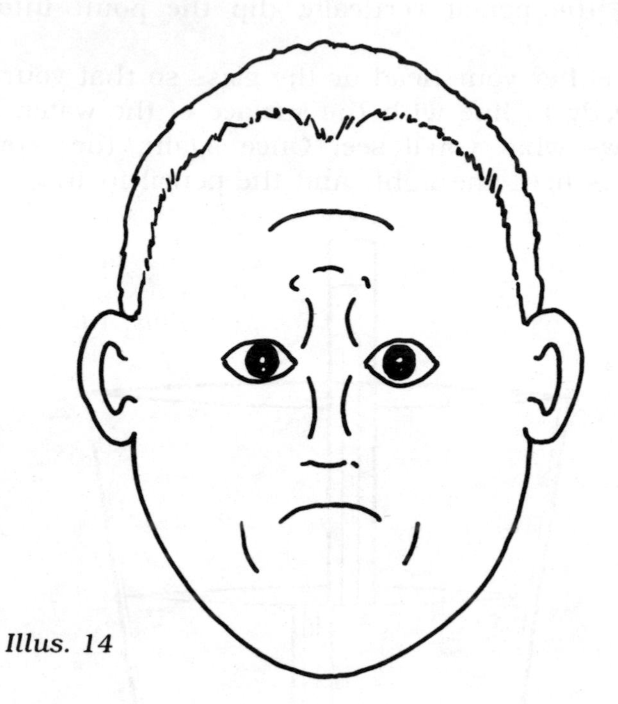

Illus. 14

Now turn the page upside down and look at the drawing again.

See how much can change with just a little movement?

• 2 •
See-Throughs

The Pinwheel

There is nothing new about a pinwheel; these toys have been around for hundreds of years. However, there is something about this toy which you may never have realized.

First, let's make a pinwheel. You'll need a piece of square notebook or typing paper. To make a rectangular piece of paper square, fold the bottom corner up as in Illus. 15. Cut away the shaded part of the paper. Unfold the paper and you have a perfect square.

Illus. 15

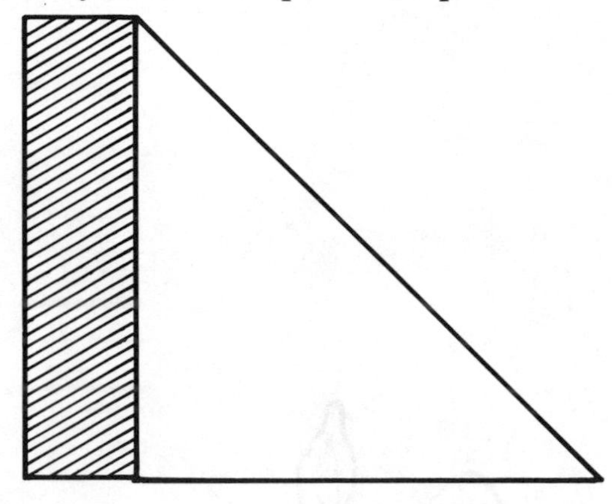

Make four cuts in this square piece of paper along the four dark lines in Illus. 16. Each of these lines runs exactly halfway to the center.

Illus. 16

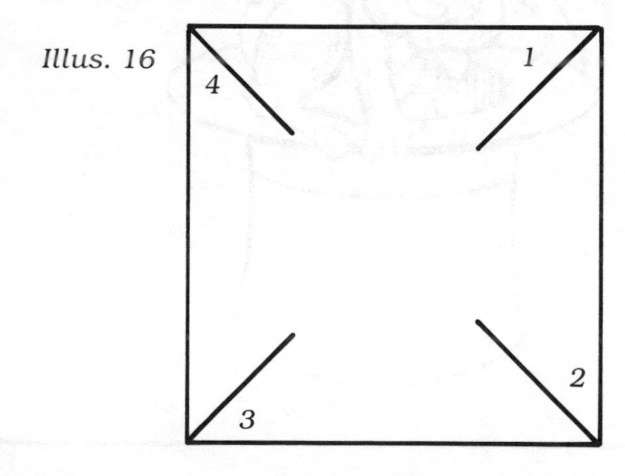

The four lines in Illus. 16 each have a number. Begin with point 1 and bend (don't fold) it down to the middle of the paper. Push a pin through a point about ¼ inch from the tip of the point.

Now bend point 2 over to the middle so that it is under point 1. Push the pin through it as well.

Do the same for points 3 and 4 and you have just about finished making your pinwheel.

It is a good idea to put a tiny dot of glue on the bottom of each point before adding the next point. This will keep the pinwheel's points together and make it spin better. If you don't have glue handy a little piece of transparent tape works just as well. Be sure to glue or tape the last point to the main part of the pinwheel.

Mount your pinwheel on a long pencil with an eraser. Just push the point of the pin into the eraser and the pencil becomes the handle of the pinwheel.

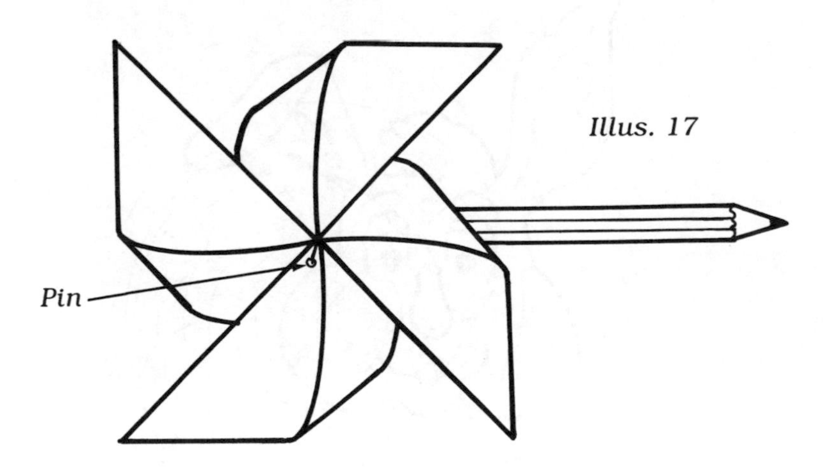

Illus. 17

Hold the pinwheel in front of you so that the curved parts of the blades face forward. As you begin to walk, the wheel should spin, and the faster you walk, the faster it spins.

Now look at something in front of the pinwheel as it spins. You can look right through the spinning pinwheel blades and see perfectly.

Examine your pinwheel, and you can easily see there is just as much paper as there is open space. Yet when the pinwheel spins rapidly you can see perfectly through its blades. The solid part almost vanishes.

Once again, afterimage is the culprit. Your eyes are focused on the object behind the pinwheel, so you actually only see the pinwheel in fleeting glimpses. Since your mind is also focused on the object instead of the pinwheel, it holds onto this image as long as possible. By the time it fades, your eyes see the object between the pinwheel parts again.

The Spinning Disc

Make a disc about 6 inches across out of the side of a cereal box or some other stiff material. If you don't have a compass, just draw around a dish or the lid from a small pan.

Now cut four round holes in the disc as in Illus. 18. Each of these holes should be about the size of a nickel. Make the outside edge of each little hole about ¾ inch from the outer edge of the disc.

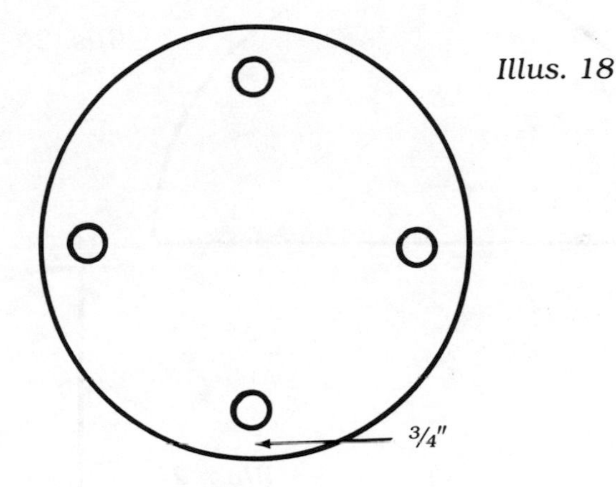

Illus. 18

Now make two very small holes as shown in Illus. 19. Each of these holes must be exactly ½ inch from the center of the disc.

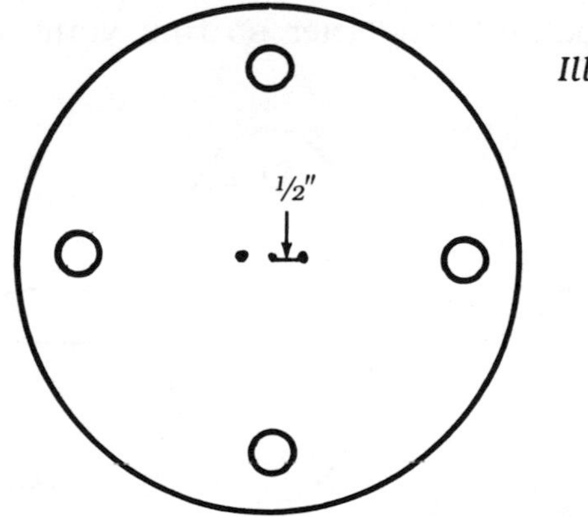

Illus. 19

If you used a compass to draw your disc it is easy to find the center, but if not, trace around the disc on a sheet of paper. Cut out the paper circle which is the same size as your disc. Fold the circle in the middle and crease the fold, so that it looks like Illus. 20. Fold it double again so that it looks like Illus. 21. Place the curve of this folded paper over the outside of your disc, and the point of the paper is the center of the disc.

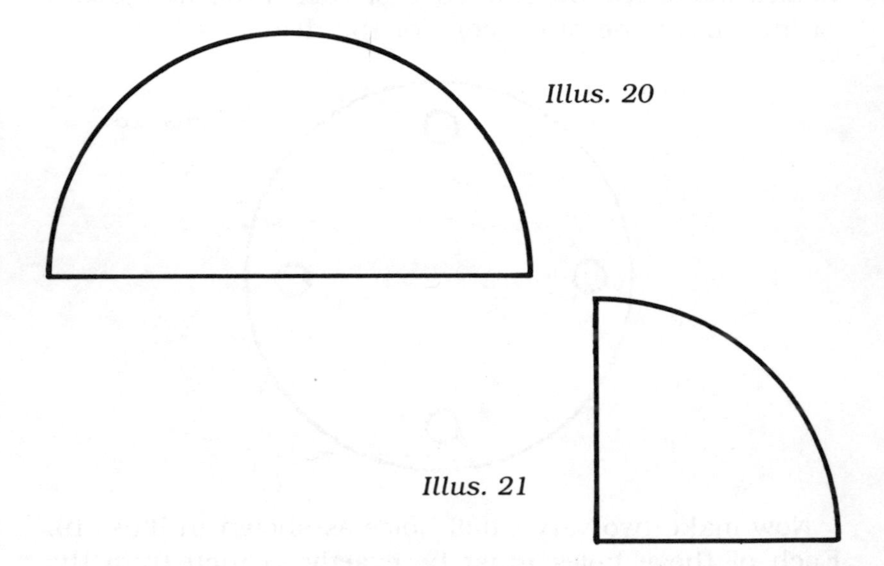

Illus. 20

Illus. 21

Cut a piece of string about 4 feet long. Run both ends through the holes near the center of the disc, and tie the loose ends together so that your disc looks like Illus. 22.

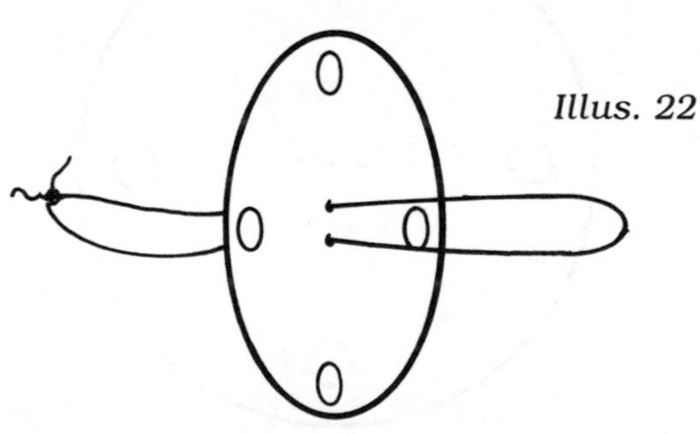

Illus. 22

Slip two or three fingers into the loop at each end of the string. Spin the disc so that it makes a number of twists in the string. Be sure the disc remains at right angles to the string. Illus. 23 shows your disc ready to go.

Illus. 23

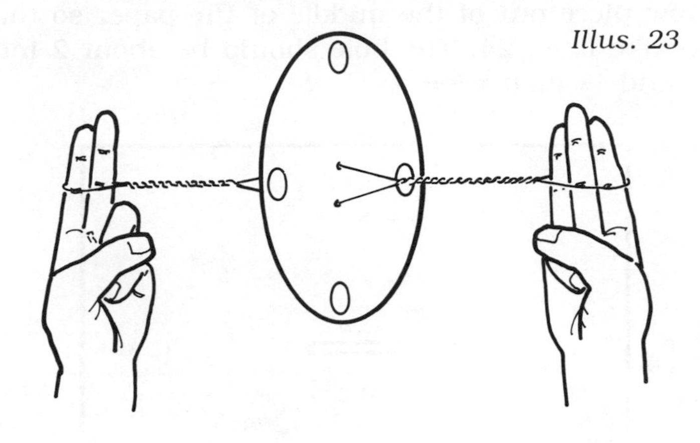

Pull your hands apart so that the disc spins as the string unwinds. Let its momentum start winding the string in the other direction. As this happens, allow your hands to begin to come together so that the string can wind up.

As the disc begins to slow, pull your hands apart and it will spin in the opposite direction. With practice, you can keep the disc spinning by moving your hands back and forth.

Now, look at the flat side of the spinning disc, and—surprise! Instead of seeing the four small holes flash past, there's a completely hollow ring. You can actually see through it as it spins.

If you have trouble keeping the disc at right angles, make one of thicker material, or, make two discs about 2 inches across, and glue one to each side of your disc around the center. Either way, all it takes is a bit of practice.

Narrow View

Moving optical illusions can take many forms. It's amazing to find out just what tricks our eyes can play on us.

Take a sheet of notebook or typing paper, and cut a narrow piece out of the middle of the paper so that it looks like Illus. 24. The hole should be about 2 inches long and ¼ inch wide.

Illus. 24

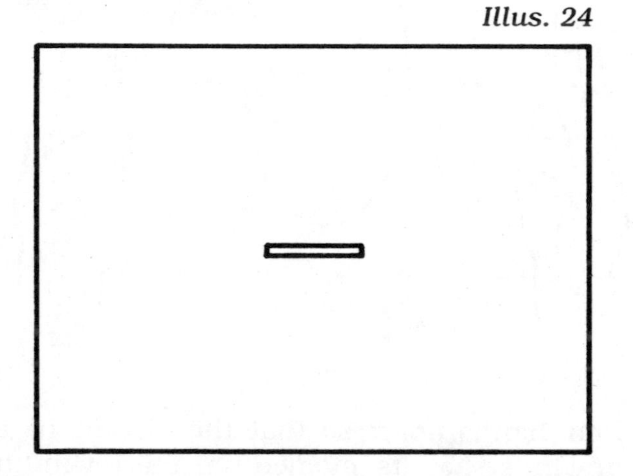

Lay the paper flat on any of the illustrations in this book. Be sure the narrow hole is over the middle of the picture. What do you see? Obviously, not much. Now begin moving the paper rapidly back and forth so that the opening slides up and down over the picture.

It takes only a few moves of the paper for you to realize that something strange is happening. You can actually see the entire picture, and the faster you move the paper, the clearer the picture becomes.

If you feel like experimenting, try this with another sheet of paper. This time make the narrow cut even narrower—less than ¼ inch across. Keep the length 2 inches.

Can you still move the paper rapidly enough to see the picture? How small can you make the cut and still be able to see a picture under the sheet of paper?

See-Through Grid

While you're looking through things, try a grid. This moving illusion has been around for many years. Your grandparents may have done it when they were children.

Start with a small piece of tracing paper. Tissue paper works well; even very thin typing paper works. Just check it by placing it over this page to make sure you can still see the print through the paper.

To make the grid, rule off a square about 2 inches in each direction of your see-through paper. Don't cut out the square because you need to have a little margin on at least one side to hold on to.

Draw parallel lines up and down every ⅛ inch until you fill the square. Then draw another set of parallel lines across the square. These lines should also be ⅛ inch apart. Your grid should now look like Illus. 25.

Illus. 25

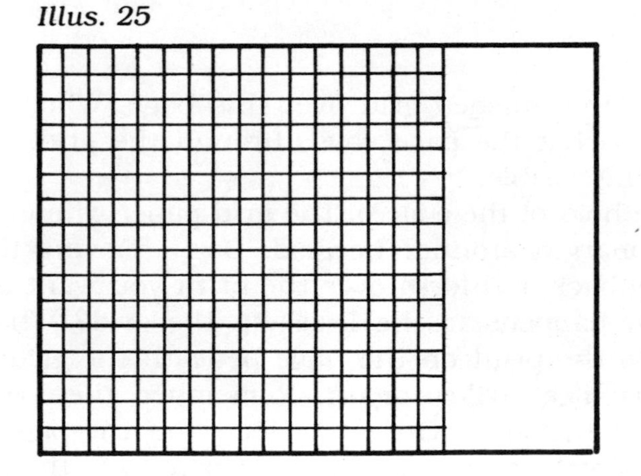

Now draw parallel diagonal lines every ⅛ inch from right to left across the square. Finish up the grid with a final series of parallel diagonal lines from left to right. The final grid is in Illus. 26.

Illus. 26

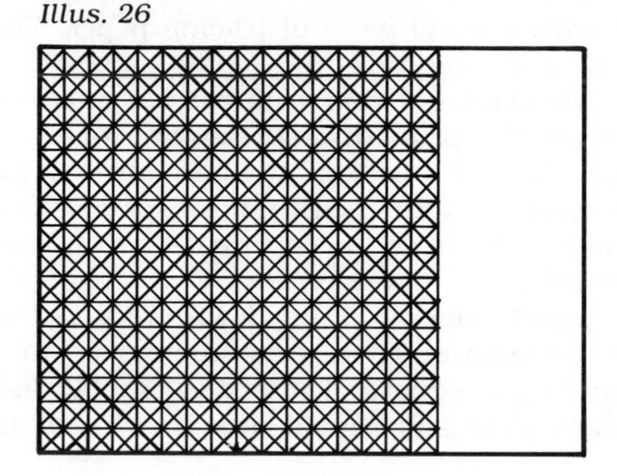

Place the finished grid over this page. When you try to read what the page says through the grid, it is almost impossible.

Take hold of the edge of the grid paper where you left some margin around the grid. Begin moving the grid rapidly back and forth over the print you want to read.

What happens to the lines on the grid? What happens to the print on the page beneath the grid?

Afterimage strikes again. Remember, there *is* space between the lines. Once you focus on the page under the grid your brain will try to help you see the page as clearly as possible. When the grid moves, your eyes will focus on the page and your brain ignores the lines that move back and forth. So, when your eyes see the grid, your brain still holds the afterimage, and as it fades, your eyes see the object again.

Seen Under Glass

Place a small, flat object on the table or on the countertop. A coin works fine; so does a paper clip or even a small piece of paper.

On top of this object, set a glass. Be sure that this is a clear glass you can see through. Look through the glass from the top and the sides. Of course, you see the object beneath the glass.

Now fill the glass with water. Get it as full as you can without spilling. Set it on top of the object. Look through the glass full of water. You'll see the object under the glass again. So, where is the illusion?

Place a saucer or a plastic lid from a butter tub on top of the glass, as in Illus. 27. Look through the side of the glass.

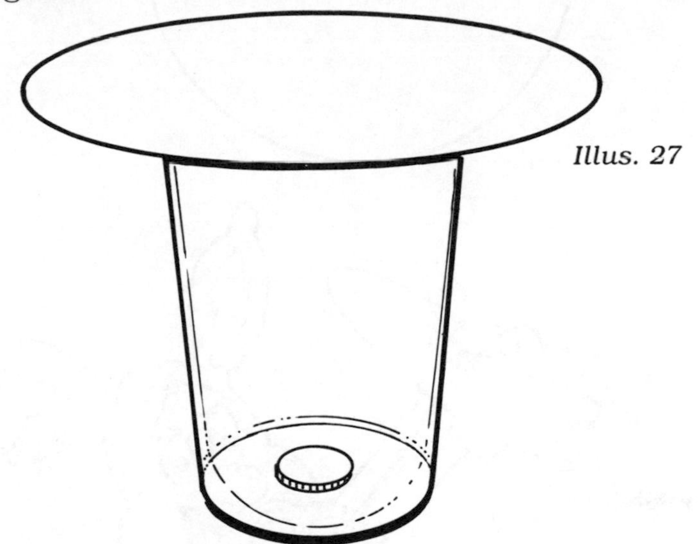

Illus. 27

Remember that when light rays pass through water they are bent or turned at a different angle. When the saucer is on top of the glass the light rays which bend towards the top of the glass hit the saucer, shutting them in. The light rays from the coin can't be seen, so it seems to have vanished.

Strange Motion

Cut a circle 5 inches or so across from the side of a cereal carton. Any stiff material works fine but cereal cartons are usually pretty easy to find.

Make the cut shown in Illus. 28.

Illus. 28

Be careful when you poke the point of your scissors through the cardboard. You want a hole in the cardboard, not in your finger.

The little cut should be 1 inch long, ⅛ inch wide, and about ½ inch from the outside of the cardboard disc.

Next find the exact center of the disc and make a small hole there. If you forgot how to find the circle's center, look back at page 26. It works every time.

Push a pencil through the center so that it looks like Illus. 29.

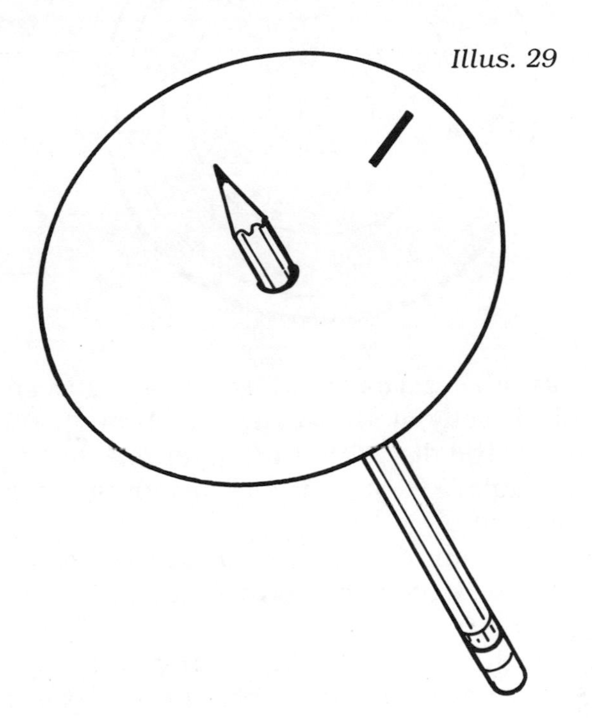

Illus. 29

Hold the pencil between your hands. Keep both hands flat and press them together firmly against the pencil.

Move your hands rapidly up and down, so that the pencil spins back and forth between your hands. When the pencil spins, the disc will spin as well.

If the disc slips on the pencil use several pieces of tape to fasten it to the main part of the pencil.

Start a record turntable without a record on it. Place a piece of paper or cardboard on one side of the turntable, as in Illus. 30.

Illus. 30

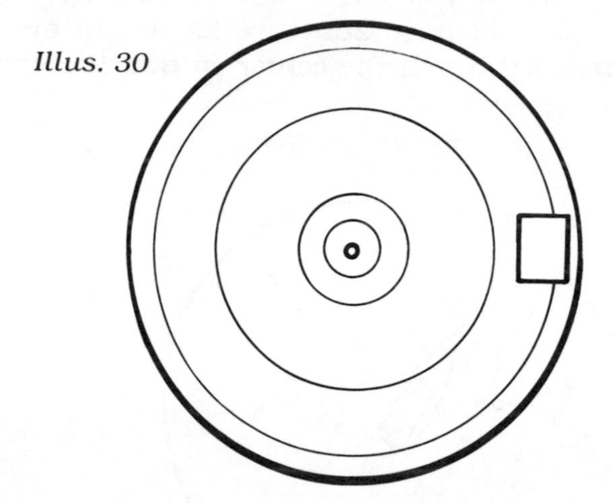

As the turntable turns, spin the disc between your hands. Look directly at the turntable through the narrow little slit in the disc. What's happening to the paper on the turntable? Is it actually jumping back and forth? It can't be.

Try spinning your disc faster or slower to see how this affects the way the paper on the turntable seems to act.

Do you have fluorescent lights around you? These are the ones which have the long tubes. Lots of classrooms have them.

Look at a fluorescent light through your spinning disc. If you get the speed just right you can get the light to blink on and off like a flashing strobe light you would see at a concert or disco.

• 3 •
Spots and Colors

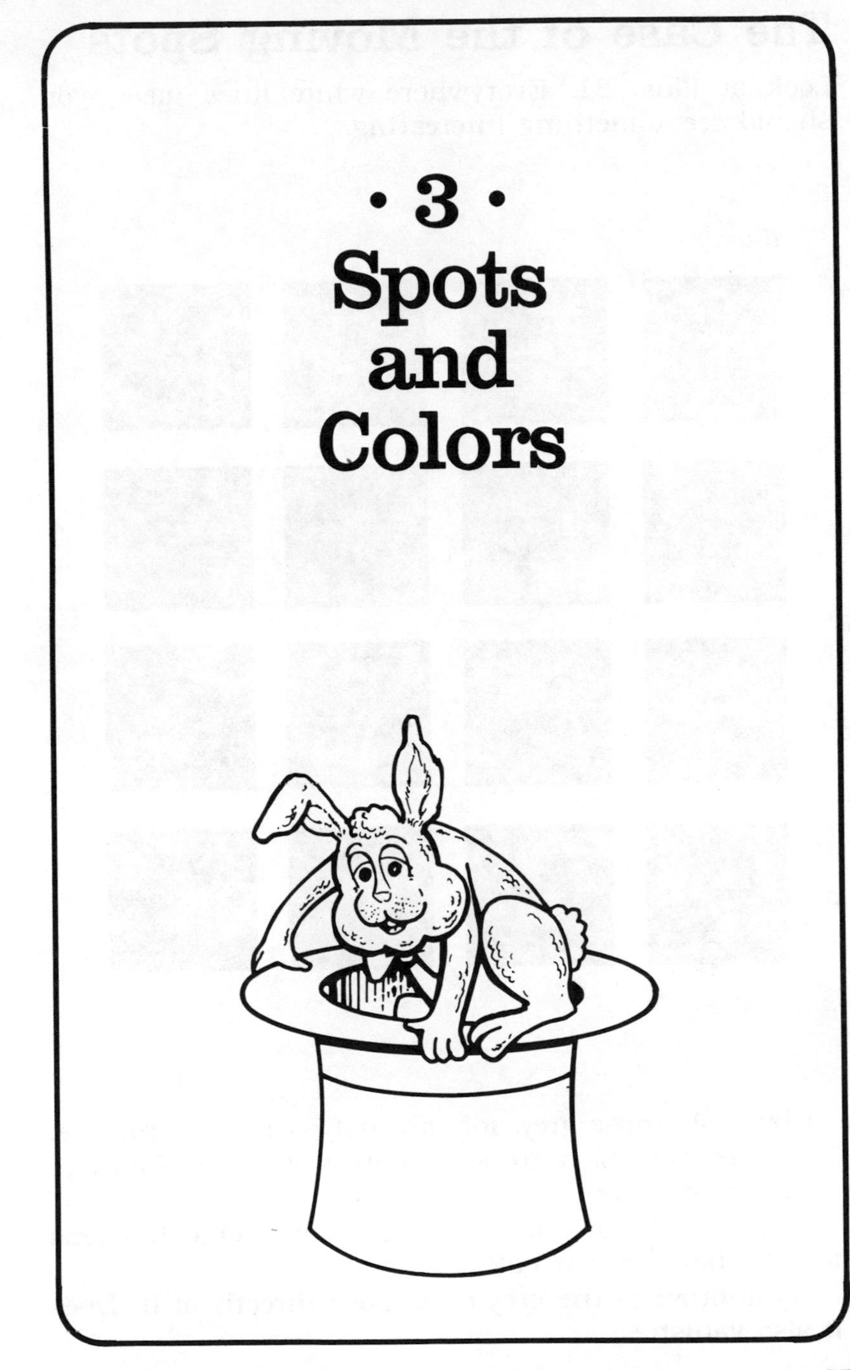

The Case of the Moving Spots

Look at Illus. 31. Everywhere white lines meet, you should see something interesting.

Illus. 31

Obviously those grey dots are not part of the picture. Therefore, they have to be an optical illusion. Now, let's make them move.

Stare directly at one of the grey dots. What happens to it? Where does it go?

Try another of the grey dots. Look directly at it. Does it also vanish?

Floaters

Make a tiny hole in a piece of paper or a white file card. This is called a pinhole. If the hole you make is a little larger than a pinhole, that is just fine.

Now hold the tiny hole up to your eye. Stare at a light through the hole. *Don't stare at the sun.* A shaded lamp should be bright enough. Illus. 32 shows how to manage this.

Illus. 32

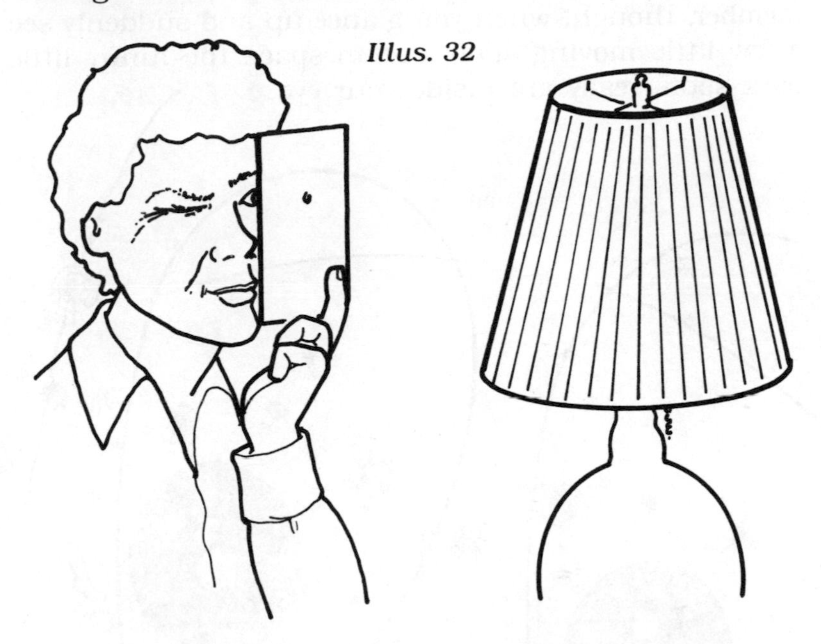

Close the eye not looking through the pinhole, and focus on the hole itself; you will begin to see slow-moving little circles or rings.

After a minute check your other eye. The same sorts of hollow little circles should appear.

These slowly moving little fellows are called floaters. They actually move inside your eyeball. These tiny floaters are normal and do not mean anything is wrong with your eyes. From time to time little cells inside the eye come free and float in the liquid which fills your eyeball. That's why they're called floaters.

Most people also have another kind of floater inside their eyes. The way to check for these is to look down at the floor for a few seconds; then quickly raise your head and look at a light-colored wall. You may see one or more tiny little dark colored objects which seem to be between you and the wall.

Don't worry if you can't see any floaters. Older people are more likely to have them than children, and some young people don't seem to have them at all. Remember, though, when you glance up and suddenly see a few little moving spots out in space the funny little dark spots really are inside your eye.

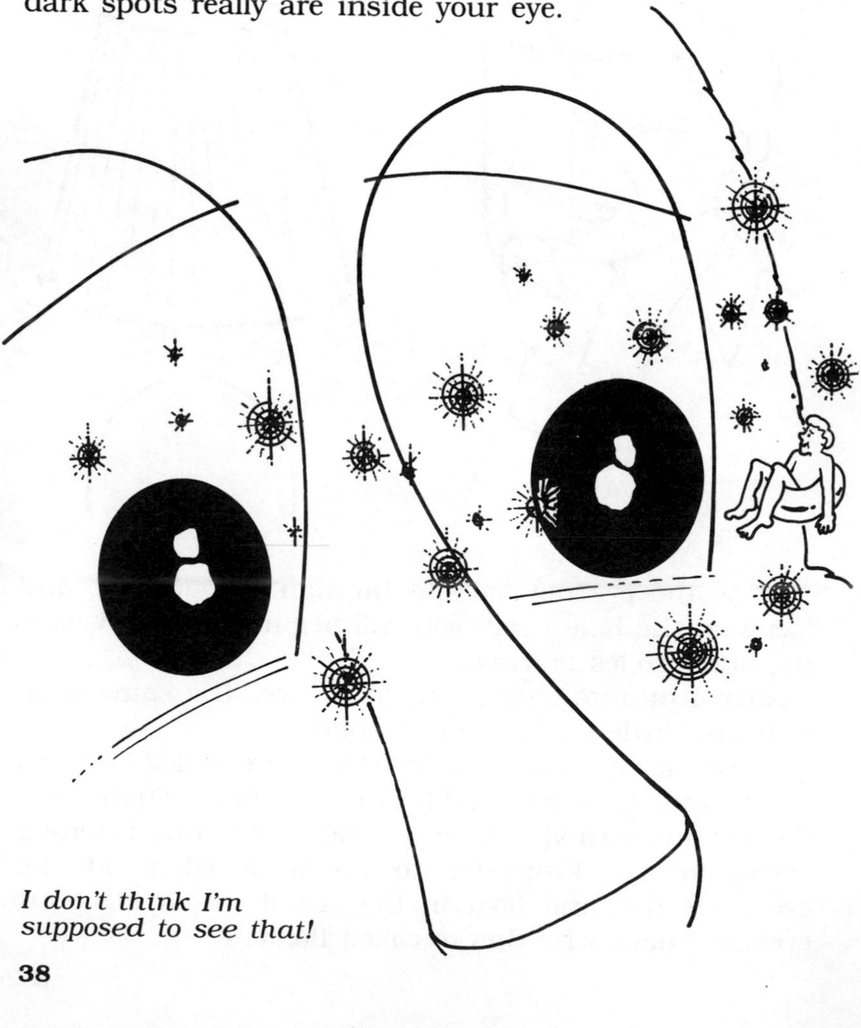

I don't think I'm supposed to see that!

Colorful Illusion

Begin by making a bright orange triangle on a white piece of paper. A triangle about 1 inch high is a good size.

Now make a card with a pinhole and, holding the orange triangle out in front of you, peer through the hole in the card as in Illus. 33.

Illus. 33

What happens to the brightness of the orange triangle? Did the color fade or is it just an illusion?

Try this one. On a white piece of paper make a solid red square, about 1 inch across. Stare directly at it for about thirty seconds; then look away and focus on a white piece of paper or a white wall. Within a few seconds a square will appear. But it won't be red!

Now color a green circle on a piece of white paper. It's okay to use the paper with the red square, but fold the red square over out of sight. Stare at it intently for half a minute; then look at a sheet of clean white paper. What color is it?

Do the same thing with the orange triangle you made before. Stare at it; see what color the orange triangle becomes when you look away.

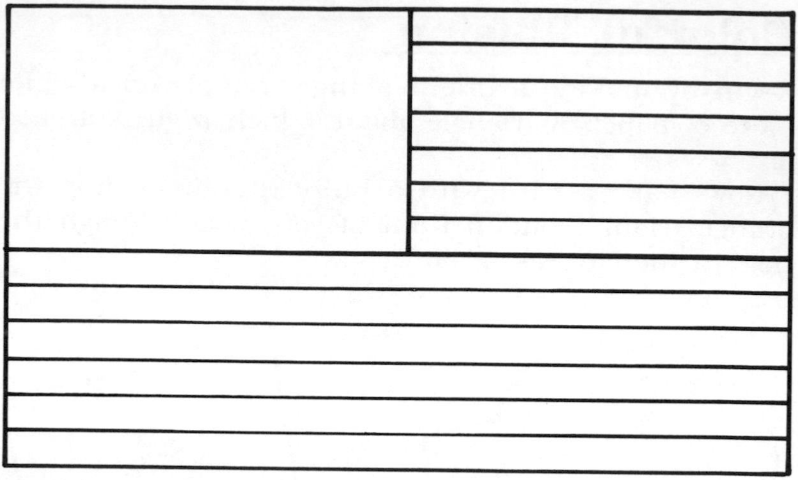

Illus. 34

Illus. 34 should be familiar to you. Make the outline of the flag about 6½ inches high × 10 inches. The smaller rectangle at the upper left should be about 5 inches wide and 3½ inches high. Each of the 13 bands should be exactly ½ inch wide.

Color the small rectangle orange; then color the top band green and the second band black, alternating the bands, green and black, all the way to the bottom. You will end up with the bottom band colored green. There should be seven green bands and six black bands. Make your colors good and dark. Somehow it doesn't look right, does it?

Now, stare intently at the finished picture for about thirty seconds; then look away at a sheet of white paper or a white wall. It should look a little more familiar now. If you want, add some black dots to the orange field. Alternate five rows of six dots with four rows of five dots. If you begin and end with a row of six dots, you've done it perfectly.

This is a project you will probably want to put up on your wall or bulletin board. Place a sheet of white paper beside it so that others can see the illusion move from the original to the plain white page.

Spinning Colors

About 150 years ago some German scientists discovered a way to make black and white drawings look colorized. They discovered a disc that is still a great illusion today.

The first disc you will make is shown in Illus. 35.

Illus. 35

Make this disc as large as you wish, but 3½ inches across is a good size. Use any stiff white material (a 4 × 5-inch file card is perfect).

If you don't have stiff white cardboard, make your circle on white paper, color it, and cut it out. Glue or tape it to any stiff material (like a cereal box).

A soft-tipped marker is excellent for coloring, but a black crayon will also do the job.

Color half the disc solid black; then put in the two sets of curved black lines. A compass or the edge of a round object can help with these curved lines.

Try to space the curves evenly. Draw them in pencil first; then go over the pencil lines with marker or crayon. If the spaces between the lines are not exactly the same the project will still work, so don't panic. Once the disc is colored it is time to see whether those German scientists knew what they were talking about.

First we need to spin the disc. There are three ways to do this.

One is to stick a straight pin through the center of the disc, making sure the head of the pin is at the front (so the disc won't spin off). Hold the pointed end of the pin tightly, and use your other hand to do the spinning.

A second way to spin is to push the point of a pencil through the disc's center. Hold the pencil between your palms and rub your hands back and forth. This spins the disc quickly in one direction, then back in the other. A straight-sided pencil works better than a round one. A couple of pieces of tape to attach the back of the disc to the sides of the pencil should also help.

The third way is to use the string spinner. If you forgot how to make one of these, look back at page 25. If you have any trouble keeping the spinner upright, just use a couple of pieces of tape on the back of the spinner so that the tape sticks to the strings as they go through the spinner. Illus. 36 shows how to do this.

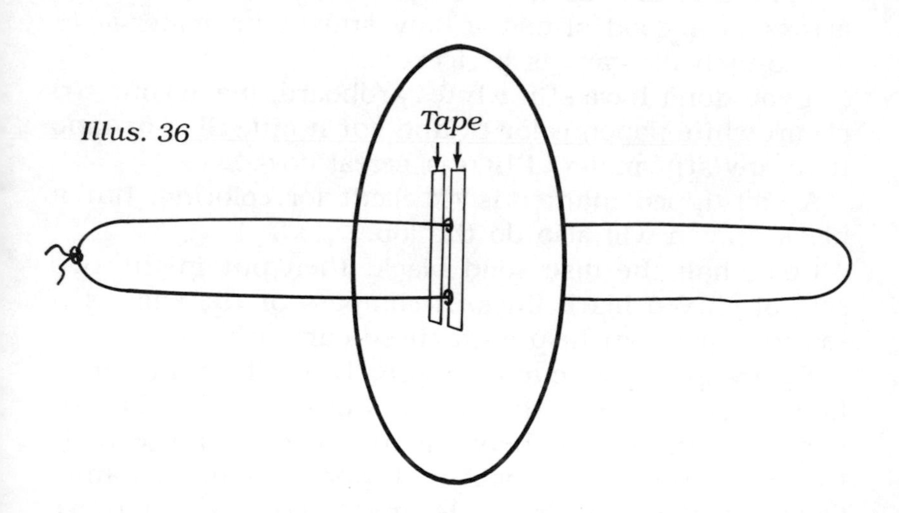

Illus. 36

Give your disc a good spin. Watch what happens to the black and white design. If you don't see the colors at first, don't give up. Spin it some more, and take a good look.

You should see brown and blue appear. When the disc turns one way, the brown is towards the outside of the disc. When it spins the other way, blue is outside. Check it for yourself.

Illus. 37 shows another black and white disc which will turn to different colors when it spins. Make it in the same way you just made the previous disc.

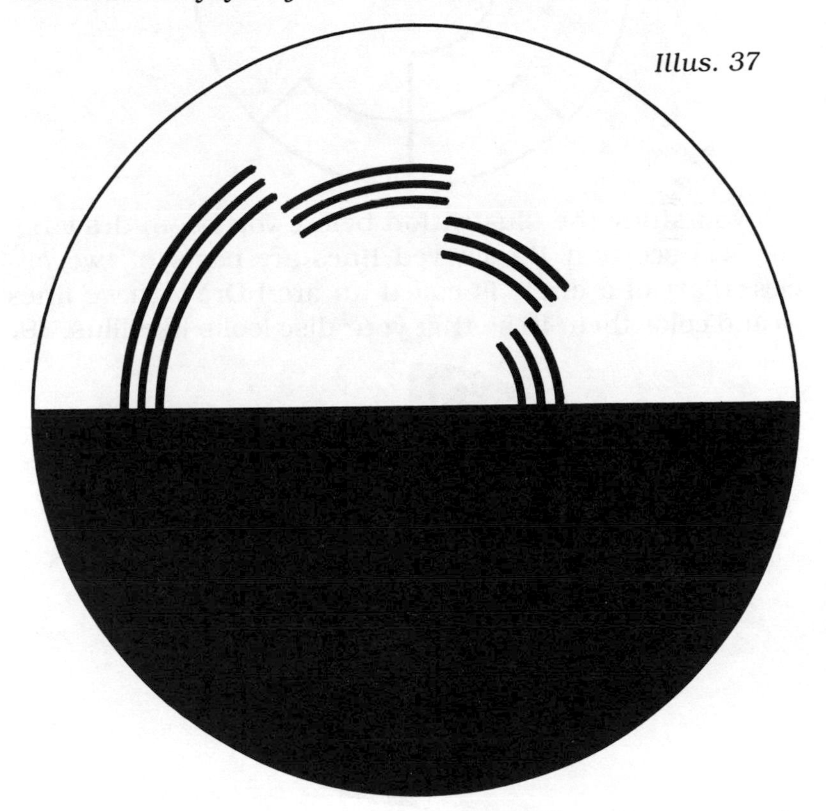

Illus. 37

When this disc spins, you should be able to spot the colors of blue, green, and brown. Just like the first disc, the colors change positions when you reverse the direction of the spin.

Let's do one more of these black and white discs before we go to a different sort of spinning color disc. Its outline can be seen in Illus. 38.

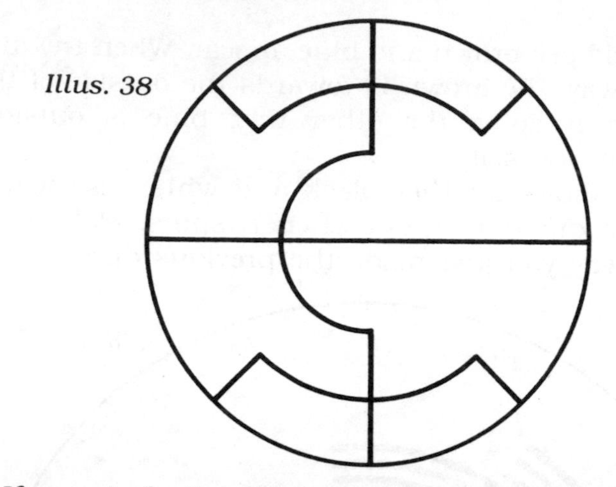
Illus. 38

If you study the illustration before you begin drawing, you will see that the curved lines are parts of two circles. (Part of a circle is called an arc.) Draw these lines in and color them in so that your disc looks like Illus. 39.

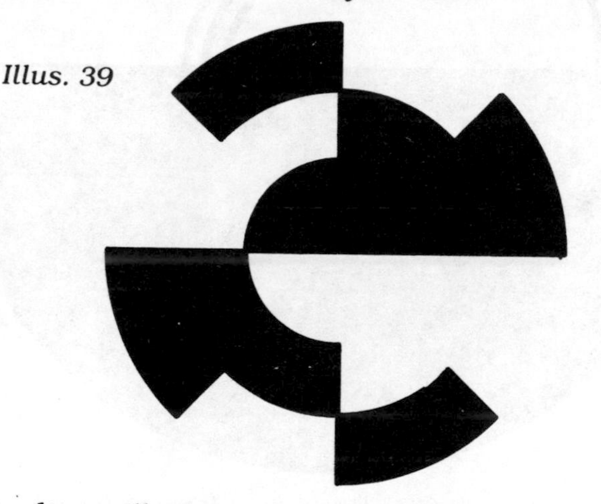
Illus. 39

This disc will give you two interesting moving optical illusions. Of course, the colors will appear. But, what happens to the solid shapes is also strange. Spin this and see for yourself.

Color Wheel

You have probably seen a color wheel in the art room at school. It shows colors in special order. It's also an interesting spinning optical illusion.

Make a disc 3½ inches across. This time make it exact, because 3½ inches across is lots easier to divide into 21 equal parts. That's right, 21.

Use a ruler to measure along the outside of the disc and place a dot every ½ inch. If all goes well you will finish with 21 equal spaces. If the last space is a tiny bit larger or smaller than the others, it won't ruin the project.

Illus. 40 shows the disc with all those lines in place. It also tells what color to use in coloring each section of the disc.

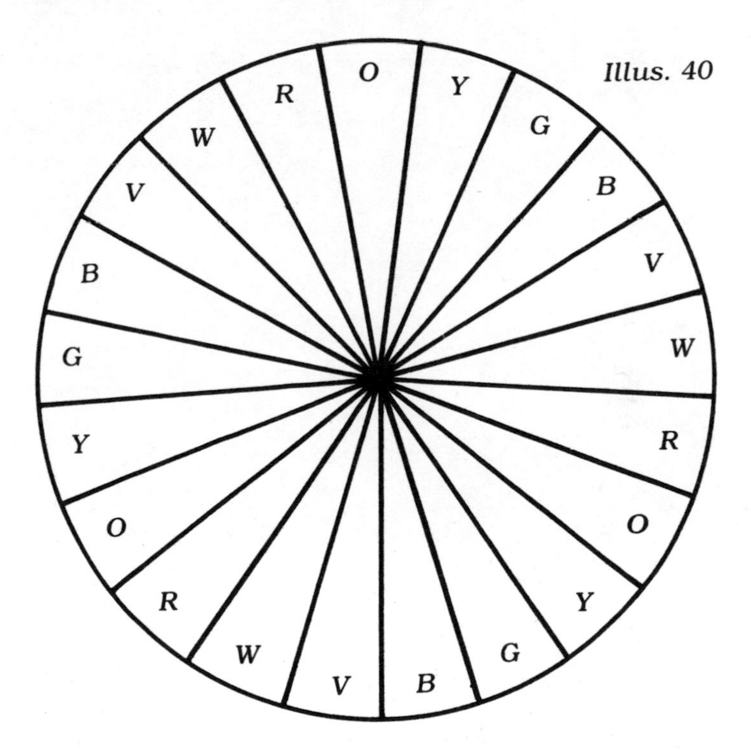

Illus. 40

Color each section of the disc according to this key: W = white, R = red, O = orange, Y = yellow, G = green, B = blue, and V = violet (purple). Colored pencils are easier to use than crayons, but crayons will do the job if you have a steady hand.

Once the disc is colored, give it a spin. As it moves faster and faster, you will see it change color. If you can get the disc to spin fast enough you will see only a white disc. More likely you will see a very light tan or even light grey.

When the disc stops, there are all those colors, still in place. The light color was just another optical illusion.

• 4 •
Done with Mirrors

Dancing Spots

Mirrors cause a number of optical illusions. Quite often we are not even aware of this fact.

In an earlier chapter we saw spots before our eyes. When you get through playing with this fantastic toy, you will see spots that move and dance so fast it seems impossible.

Begin by cutting a circle out of stiff paper or lightweight cardboard. Make this circle about 7 inches across.

Make a series of small holes around the outside of the circle as in Illus. 41.

Illus. 41

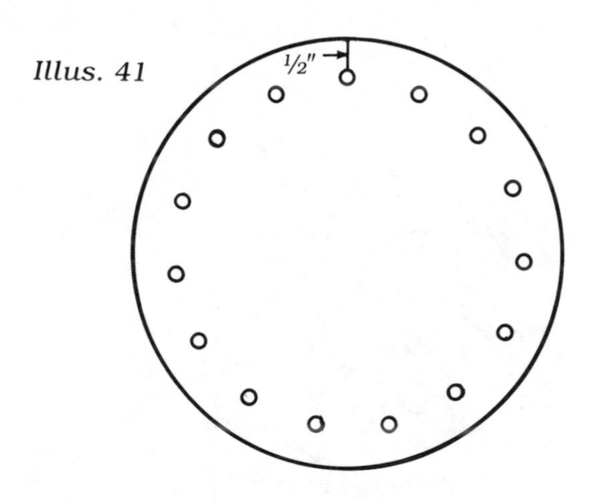

These holes should be about ½ inch in from the outside of the circle, and about 1½ inches apart. Try to space them evenly but don't get upset if a few holes are a little bit off.

A paper punch is best for this, but if you don't have one, then try a ballpoint pen that does not have a replaceable filler, because the cheaper pens are more solid and their points seem to push through the material more easily. Make sure that the pen goes all the way through so that the hole is as large as the large part of the pen, and wriggle the pen around to make sure the hole stays open. This isn't as fancy or quick as a paper punch but it will do the job.

Now cut out a paper circle about 5½ inches across. Place it on top of the disc with all the holes in it, and line up the center of the paper with the center of the cardboard. If you drew around a dish or pan lid, then find the center by folding a paper the way we did on page 26. Use a tiny piece of transparent tape to fasten the two discs together, as in Illus. 42.

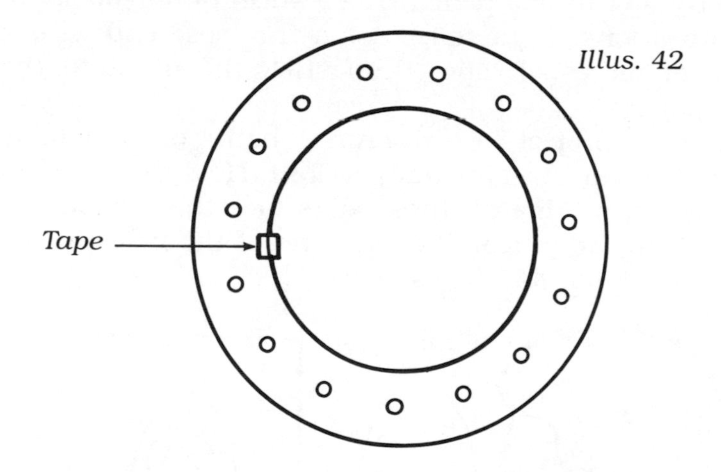

Illus. 42

Use a dark marker or crayon to make a series of dots on the paper disc, one dot in line with each hole in the outer ring. Make each dot about ¼ inch across. Don't make the dots in a circle. Place your dots in the sort of pattern as in Illus. 43, but don't try to copy the drawing exactly. The important thing is for the dark dots to be different distances from the edge of the circle.

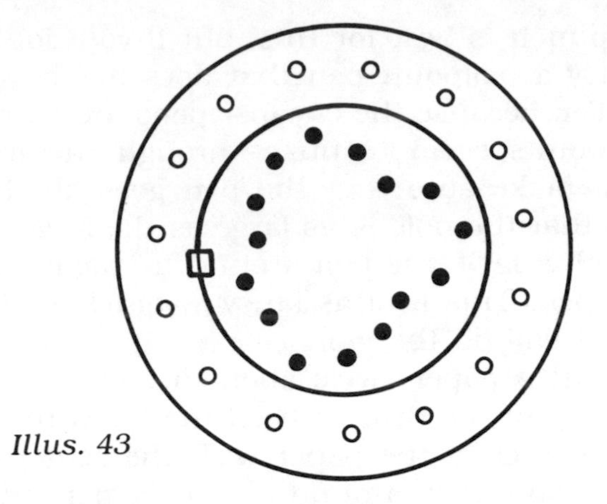
Illus. 43

Stick a straight pin through the center of both circles. Push the pin's point into the eraser on the end of a long pencil.

If you don't have a pencil, roll a sheet of notebook paper into a long, tight roll. Fasten the loose end with a couple of pieces of tape; then stick the pin into the rolled paper.

Take your project to a mirror. A bathroom mirror is excellent because it is usually well lit. Hold the wheel in front of you so that all those dots face the mirror.

Look into the mirror through one of the holes in the cardboard. Illus. 44 shows how.

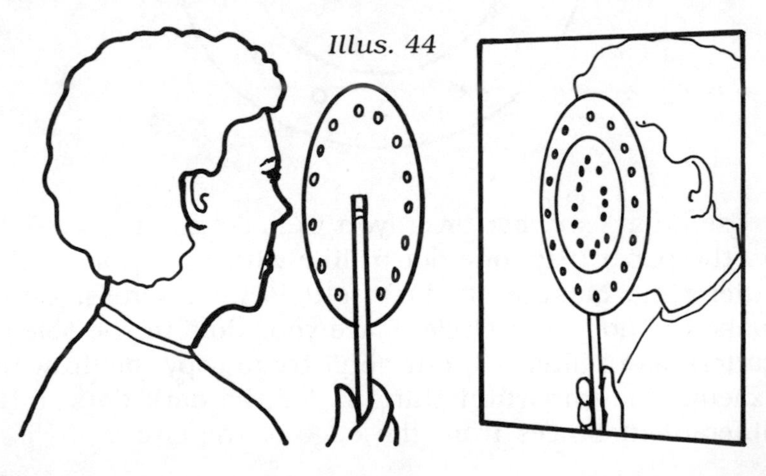
Illus. 44

Spin the wheel, looking into the mirror through the little holes which flash by.

Can you believe those dancing spots? The faster the wheel is spun the more frantic the spots become.

This is such a fantastic moving optical illusion you will not only want to show everyone, but you'll think about making things other than dots dance.

Turn your dots into little stick figures as seen in Illus. 45. Make their arms and legs good and dark. Be sure to change the positions of their arms and legs for each figure. A dark pen is perfect for making these little figures, but a marker or crayon will work well.

Illus. 45

If you find your paper circle is getting crowded with figures, you might make a slightly larger circle. Or, you can make another cardboard disc and space its holes a little farther apart.

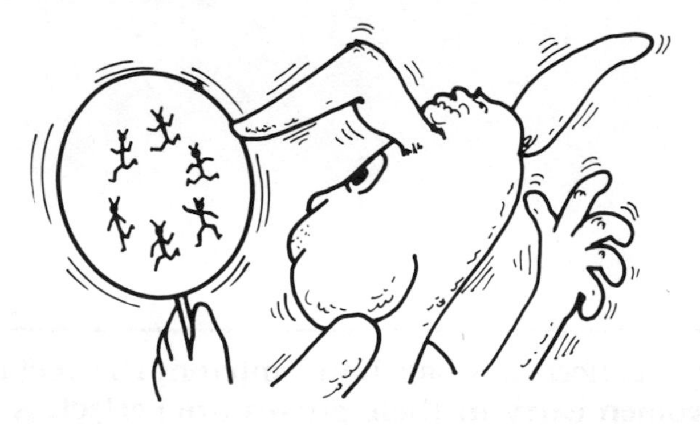

I wish I could dance like that!

Tricky Mirror

We take mirrors and the illusions they show us pretty much for granted. Here is a little stunt which will help you realize just how tricky mirrors can be.

In the middle of a sheet of notebook or typing paper, place the numbers one through ten in a pattern somewhat like the one in Illus. 46. The area in which the numbers appear is about 3 × 5 inches.

Illus. 46

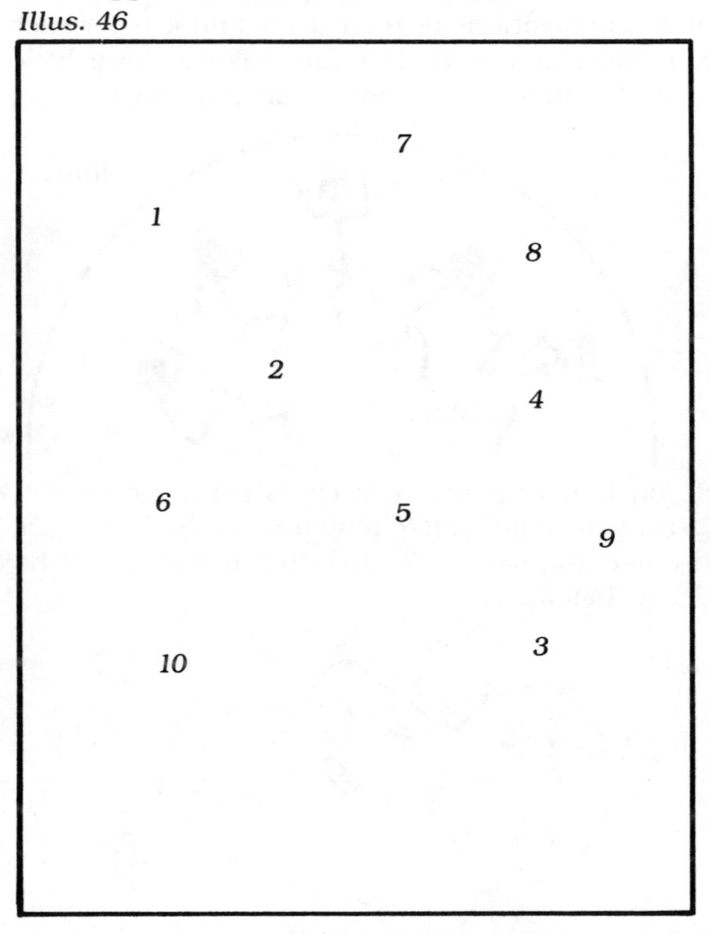

Now you need a small hand mirror. The rectangular ones women carry in their purses are perfect. A mirror with a handle will be all right, too.

Hold the mirror at one end of the paper as shown in Illus. 47.

Illus. 47

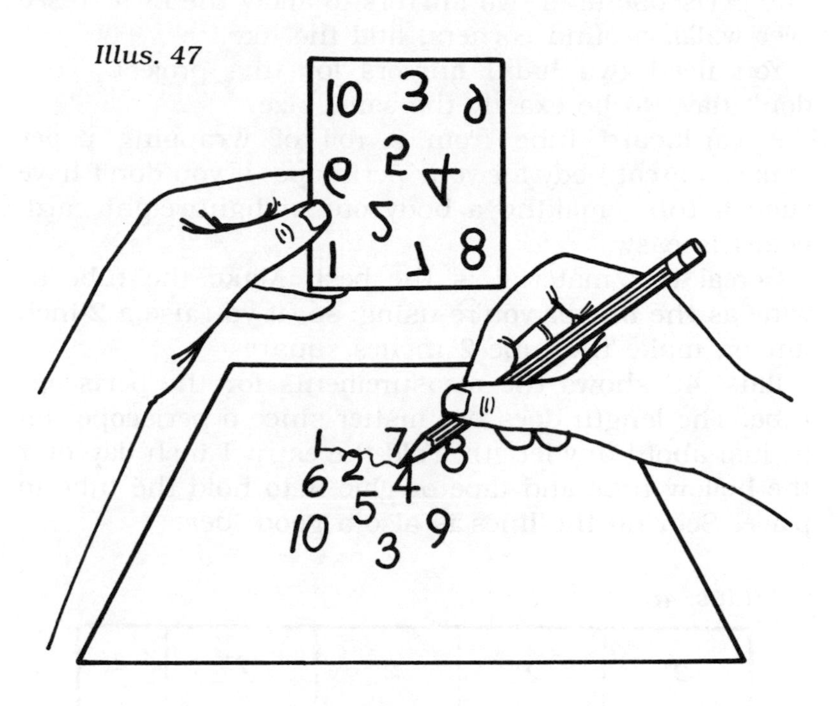

Draw a line from number one through each of the other numbers in order. Naturally you will finish up with number ten. But don't look at the paper when you draw this line. Instead, look into the mirror. To make this interesting, see how quickly you can connect all ten numbers, making the line between each pair of numbers as perfectly straight as you can. Ready, set, go!

By the time you finished this little test you learned a lot in a short time about just how tricky a mirror can be.

If you think you can improve your speed and accuracy with another attempt, feel free. Arrange the numbers in different order and have fun as you conquer this optical illusion.

Periscope

The periscope uses two mirrors to allow the user to see over walls, around corners, and the like.

You need two hand mirrors for this project. They don't have to be exactly the same size.

A cardboard tube from a roll of wrapping paper makes a great body for your periscope. If you don't have such a tube, making a body out of lightweight cardboard is easy.

Cereal box material is the best. Make the tube as wide as the mirror you're using; so, if you use a 2-inch mirror, make the tube 2 inches square.

Illus. 48 shows the measurements for the periscope tube. The length does not matter since a periscope can be just about any length. Fold the extra 1 inch flap over the hollow tube and tape or glue it to hold the tube in place. Scoring the lines is also a good idea.

Illus. 48

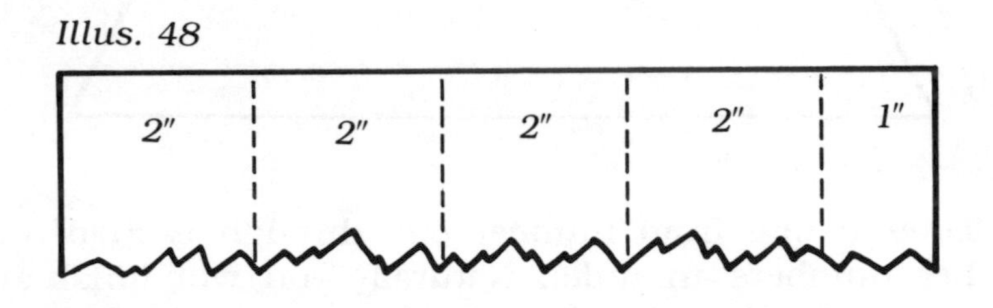

Now, very carefully, cut out a section of one end of the tube so that it looks like Illus. 49. Check the drawing carefully before you cut.

Try to make the slanting cuts 45° angles (halfway between a right angle and no angle). Be as accurate as possible, but if it's a few degrees off, it will not ruin your periscope.

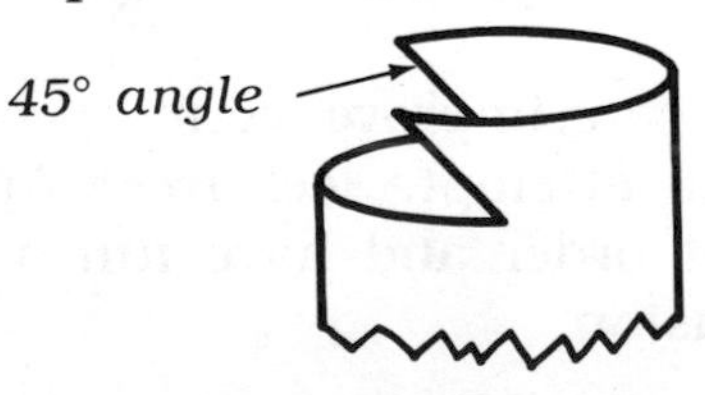

Illus. 49

Illus. 50 indicates your next step. Extend the 45° angle as shown. Cut the narrow opening just wide enough so that one of your hand mirrors can slip into the space you cut away. Be very careful not to cut these narrow slits too deep. If you do, you will end up with the end of the tube falling off or bending over.

Illus. 50

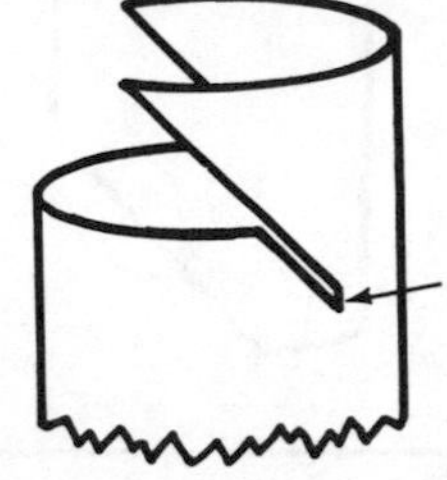

Extend cut at 45° angle on both sides

Try to make both slits at the same angle and the same length. This makes sure your mirror is centered correctly for the periscope.

Now turn your tube over. Here you'll have to be extremely accurate, because the cuts on this end must be exactly opposite the first set of cuts.

I don't think this is how the Navy does it!

Illus. 51 shows the next cut to make. Make this cut about 45° to match the bottom. The important thing is for the section you remove to be on the opposite side of the tube from the section you cut away. Illus. 52 shows how both ends of the tube look at this point.

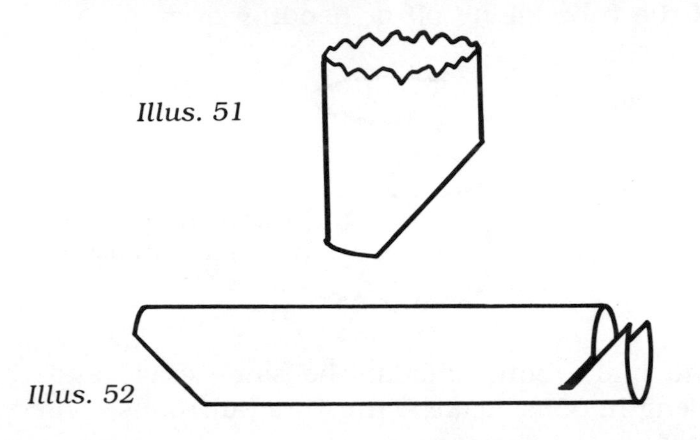

Illus. 51

Illus. 52

Now cut the two narrow slits shown in Illus. 53. These slits will hold the second mirror. Remember to be careful not to cut too deeply into the side of the tube. These slits need to be at 45° angles to the side of the tube, or parallel to the slits at the opposite end of the tube.

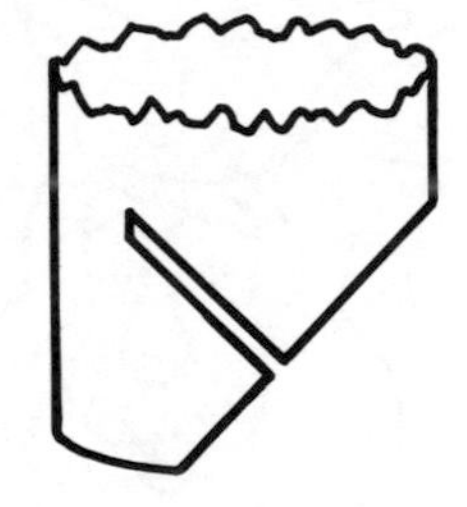

Illus. 53

It is time to place the first mirror. Go back to the end of the tube you worked on first. Slip one mirror into the two cuts as in Illus. 54. Be sure the reflecting side of the mirror faces into the tube. Tape the mirror very securely so that it can't slip out of place.

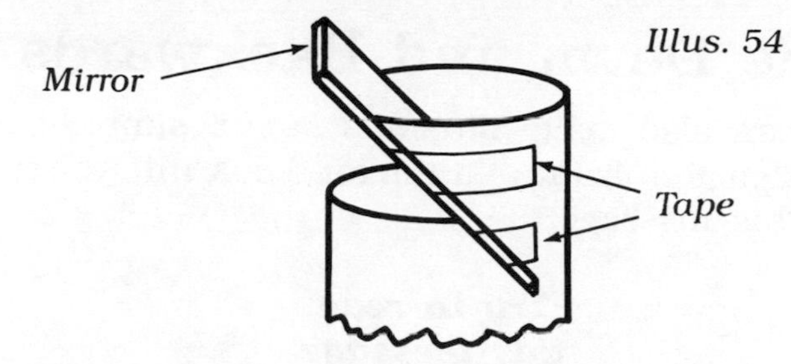

Illus. 54

Slide the bottom mirror into the bottom slits, but don't tape it into place yet. Look into the bottom mirror, as shown in Illus. 55.

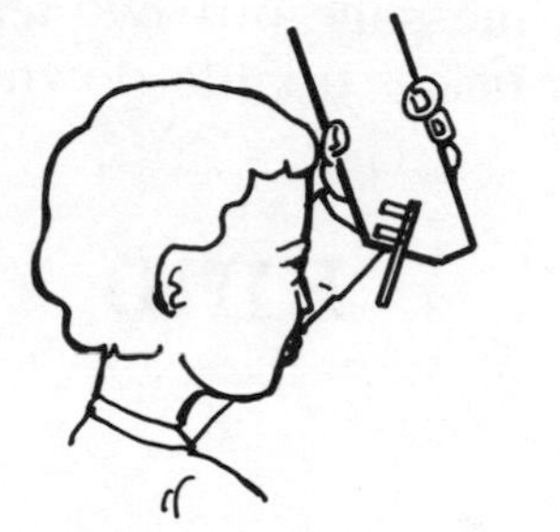

Illus. 55

Hold your periscope straight up and down. Turn the mirror towards some object. If you can see it, your mirrors are correctly aligned.

If you have to tip the periscope or raise your head up and down, the bottom mirror needs to be adjusted. Carefully tip it just a bit either up or down. At some point you will suddenly see what is reflected from the top mirror. Hold the bottom mirror in that position and tape it into place.

Sometimes you'll have to make the narrow cuts for the bottom mirror a bit wider in order to adjust the mirror's angle. This is all right to do, but don't make them very much wider, or the mirror will move too far.

Once the mirrors are adjusted and taped into place, your periscope is ready for use. Look over objects, around corners, and even into places you can't stick your head. It is great fun. What's more, when others see what you have made they will want to build one for themselves.

Upside Down and Backwards

Mirrors can also make illusions out of simple things. Hold this page in front of a mirror. Look into the mirror to read this message.

Try to read this message in a mirror.

Now that you have seen the first reflected illusion, check this next message out by viewing it in a mirror. Read the words below upside down in a mirror.

KIND

KID **NOON**

COD

What caused the different sort of reflected illusion with these words?

Write some words of your own or even compose a short message which will result in the same sort of reflected image you just saw. Just to be sure you have the idea, check your message in the mirror!

· 5 ·
Cuts and Folds

Curved Illusions

Fold a sheet of notebook paper in half. Draw the outline of the shape seen in Illus. 56 on one side of the paper. Make the drawing 6 or 7 inches long.

Illus. 56

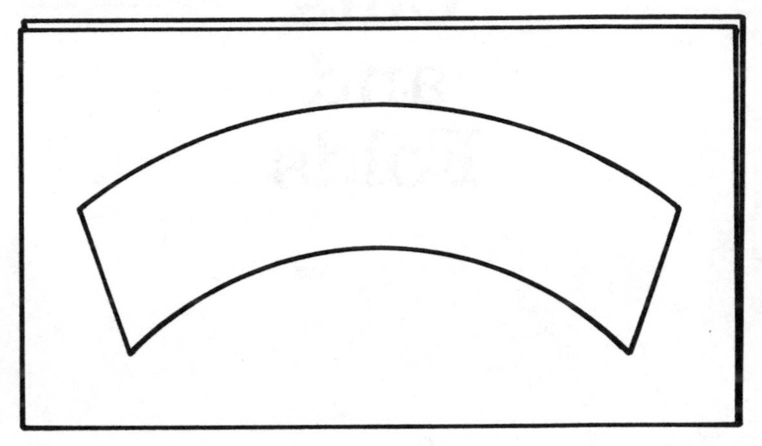

While the paper is still folded, cut out the shape. Be sure to hold the paper firmly so that the bottom half doesn't slip while you are cutting. It is very important that the two pieces be exactly the same size.

Once the two curved figures are cut out, place them side by side on the table or desk in front of you. Now, change their positions so that the one that was on the right is now on the left. Now what happens?

What happens is that putting the short-curved line next to the long-curved side creates an illusion of size.

Try moving the two pieces to different locations. Once you have convinced yourself the differences in size are just an illusion, challenge others to tell you which of the two pieces is larger. Just be sure that no one sees the two pieces except when they are side by side.

Square and Not Square

Fold another piece of paper in half. Draw the square shown in Illus. 57 on the folded paper. A 2 × 2-inch square is good.

Illus. 57

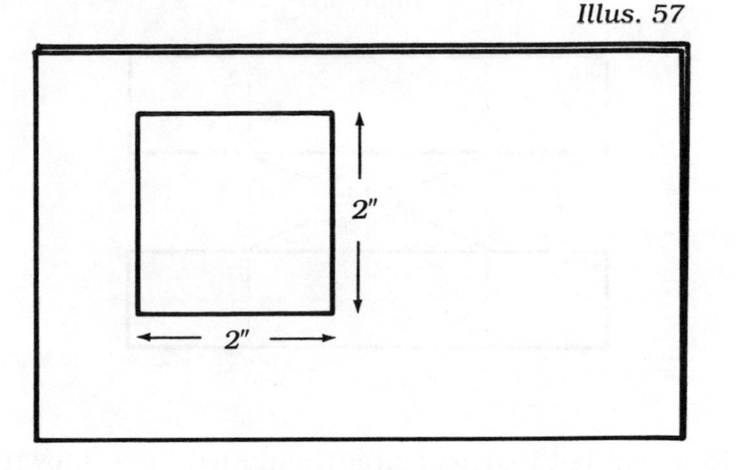

Hold the paper tightly so that you can cut out two squares at a time. Once the two squares are cut out, trim about ⅛ inch off the side of one of the squares. Leave the other square exactly square in shape.

Now for the illusion. Place the two squares (one isn't really square any more) side by side, and leave about 1 inch between them. Be sure the one you trimmed has its short distance vertical.

Look at the two. Which one is the perfect square?

Trade places with the two. Now which one is it?

Move them a little farther apart and see if this changes the illusion; then see whether a light or a dark background makes any difference.

When you are sure which piece is the perfect square, show these two pieces to others and ask them which is the perfect square.

A Matter of Folding

Cut two strips of paper exactly alike: 8 inches long and 1½ inches wide. The easiest way to do this is to cut two layers of paper at the same time.

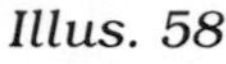

Illus. 58

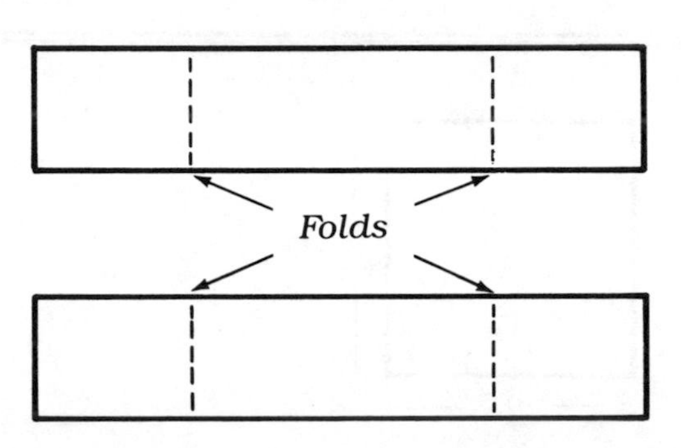

Now fold both strips along the dotted lines shown in Illus. 58. Hold the two strips on top of each other, so that the folds match perfectly. Now fold the ends of one strip outward, so that the ends point away from the middle, and fold the other strip inward, so that the ends point towards the middle. This is shown in Illus. 59.

Illus. 59

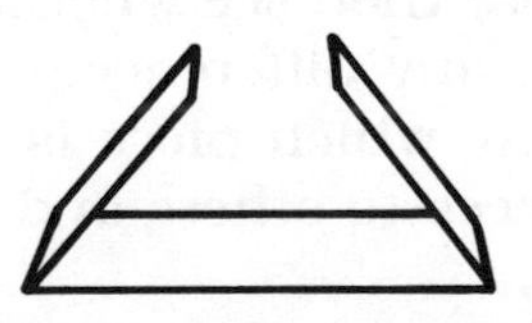

Place the strip with its ends folded in flat on a table or desk. The ends should stick up into the air.

Place the other strip 6 or 8 inches in front of the first strip. Place this strip on its side as in Illus. 60.

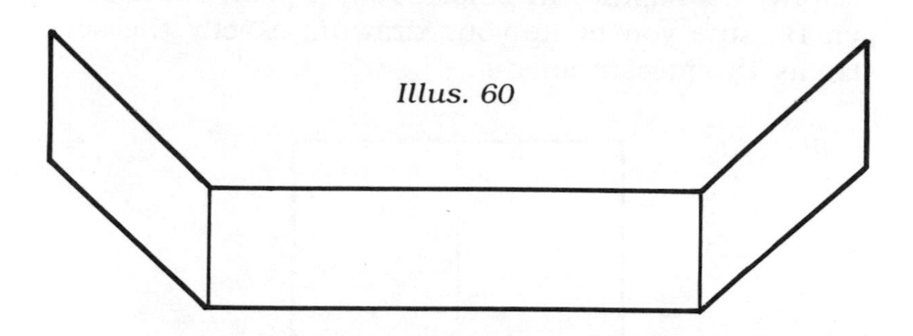

Illus. 60

Have you created an optical illusion? Move the two strips around a bit and see if they remain the same. Again, your perception has been altered because of the folds.

Now take your two paper strips and challenge someone to tell you which middle is longer.

I give up!

Illusion or Not?

For this optical illusion you need only one thickness of paper.

Draw the diagram in Illus. 61 on a plain sheet of paper. Be sure you make your drawing exactly the same size as the measurements.

Illus. 61

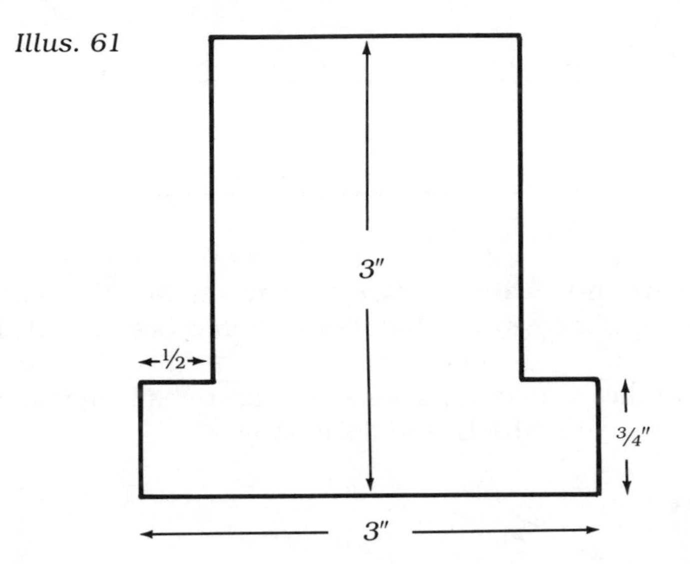

Carefully cut out the drawing and place it on the table. You know the measurements. Compare the height of the cutout with its width. Which are you going to believe—your eyes or your ruler?

Of course, you need to find someone to ask whether this figure is taller or wider. Most people will find the illusion just as tricky as you do, because the human eye and brain are easily confused by shapes and sizes.

The two small pieces at each side give your brain a misleading clue. The main part of the shape extends upwards and is wide, so your brain has a feeling of large size. Your attention is thus pulled up instead of to the left or right. This gives you the feeling that the picture is taller than it really is.

Colored Bars

Prepare for this optical illusion by cutting two strips of white paper exactly the same size. Cut them both at the same time, and make them ½ inch wide and 1½ inches long.

You now need some colored paper, the darker the better. Cut two strips of colored paper 1 inch wide. Make one strip 8 inches long, and the second 4 inches long.

Lay the colored strips side by side in front of you with the short strip nearer to you. Illus. 62 shows the way.

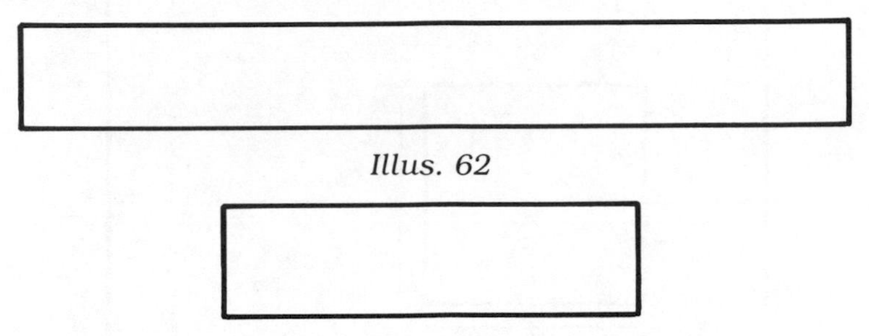

Illus. 62

Now place one of the short, white strips of paper in the exact center of each colored strip. Check the result. Which piece of white paper appears longer?

Try moving the white pieces around on the colored strips. Place them near the ends; then put one white strip at the right end of the short colored piece and the other white strip at the left end of the long colored piece. How does this affect the illusion?

Try making a strip out of paper of a different color; then try making a dark short piece exactly the same size as the white short piece. Cut a light strip of paper to replace one of the longer colored pieces. Does this affect the illusion?

In case your friends and family are beginning to catch on and have started saying, "They look different but I know they have to be the same," change tactics: Trim just a bit from the end of one of the small strips; then present the illusion.

Dark and Light

For this optical illusion you need a piece of plain white paper and another of colored paper. Again, the darker the better.

Draw a square on the white paper as in Illus. 63. Make this square about 3 inches on each side.

Illus. 63

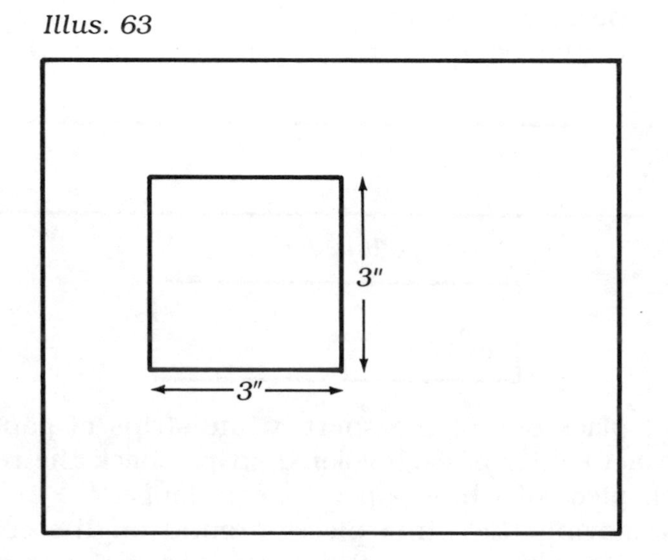

Hold the two pieces of paper, one on top of the other, and cut out the square.

Place the two squares on the table in front of you. Does one seem larger? Which one?

Try moving them about, and try different combinations.

The reason colors create so many optical illusions is that some colors are more dominant, or powerful, than others. Light colors, like white, blend, or get "swallowed," by darker colors when your eye sees them on top of one another.

There's an Angle

Cut a strip of paper 1 inch wide and 8 or 9 inches long. Fold it along the dotted lines seen in Illus. 64. Make each fold exactly 2½ inches from the end of the paper.

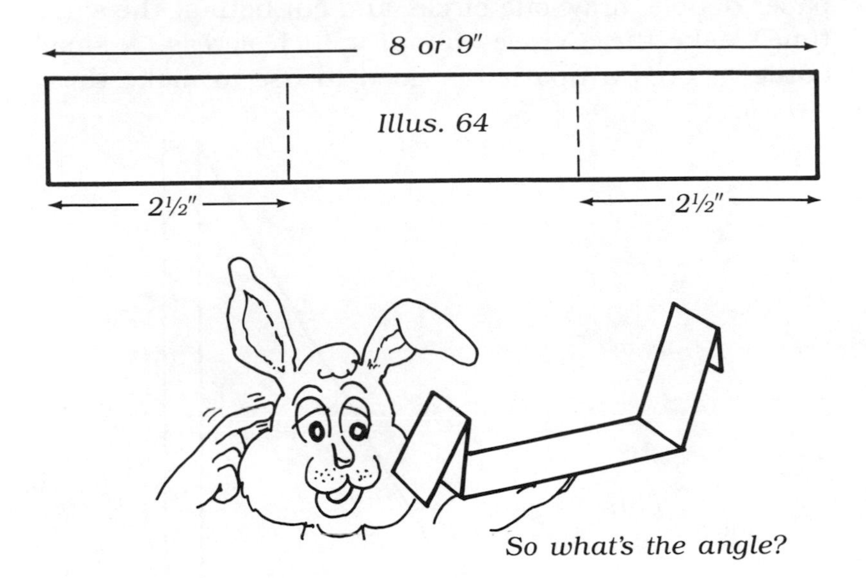

Illus. 64

So what's the angle?

Fold side A down so that its end sticks up only about 1 inch from the rest of the paper; then fold B so that its end stands up about 2 inches.

Set the paper out in front of you so that it rests on its middle part. Which folded end seems longer?

Change the angles a bit. Press side A down closer to the rest of the paper and let side B stick almost straight up. This should change the illusion a bit.

Try letting side A stick up about 1 inch or so and folding side B back to the right so that it extends way out to the right of the rest of the paper strip. What happens now?

This is obviously a good one to share with your friends. If you want to be tricky, trim just a little off the end of side B. This will keep everyone from automatically assuming everything is always exactly the same.

Circles and Angles

Begin by cutting a triangular piece of plain white paper to match Illus. 65. Cut two smaller circles from a piece of colored paper. To make them the same size, fold the paper double, draw one circle, and cut both at the same time. Make these circles about 1 inch across. A small bottle or even a quarter is good to use to make these circles.

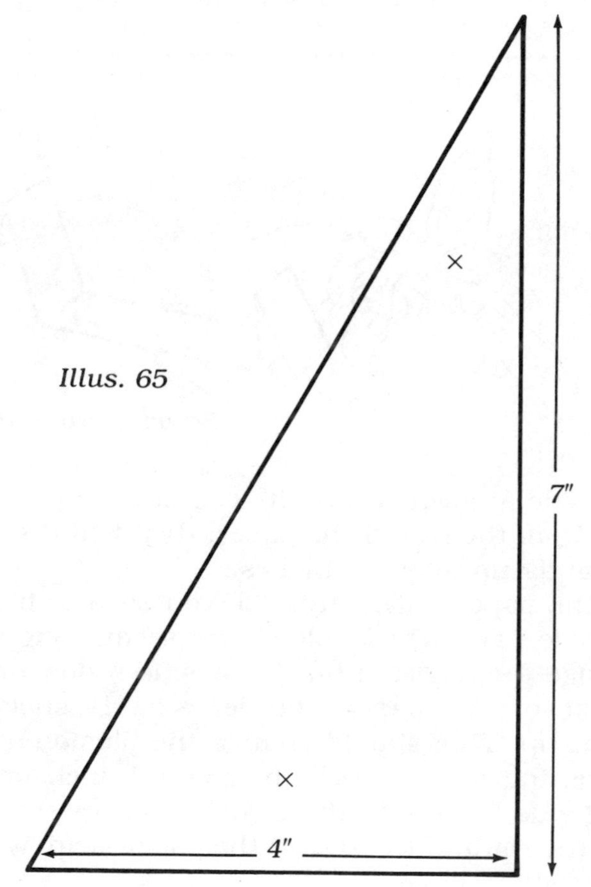

Illus. 65

Place the circles on the little ×'s in Illus. 65. Which circle appears larger?

Move the circles around a little on the triangle to see how this changes things.

Another Angle

Cut two strips of paper, each 1 inch wide. Plain paper is perfect for this optical illusion. One strip should be 3 inches long and the other 6 inches long.

Fold the long strip in half, and place it on its side as in Illus. 66.

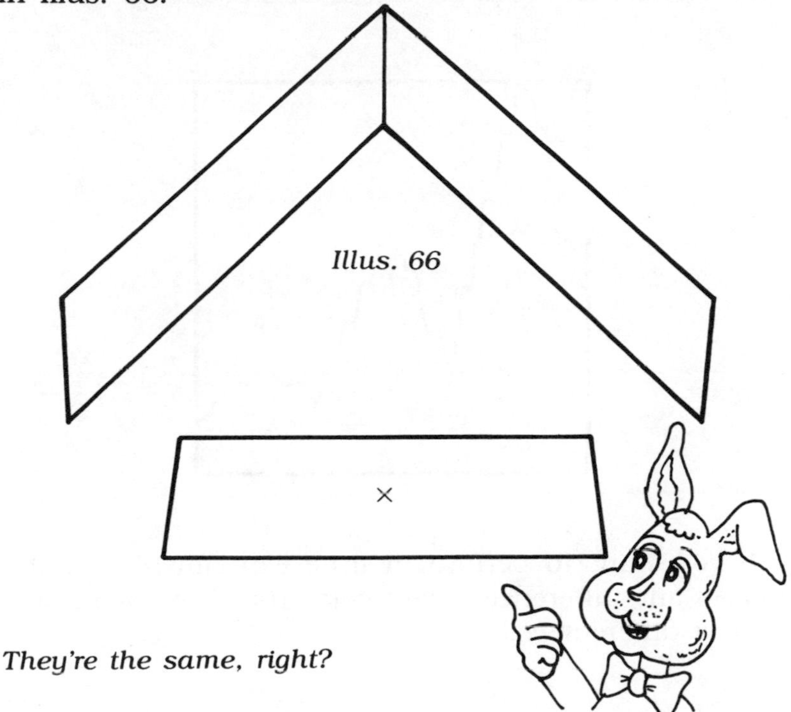

Illus. 66

They're the same, right?

Place the shorter strip flat on the table in front of the open part of the longer strip (the small × in Illus. 66).

Now which seems longer? What do your eyes tell you?

This is another good optical illusion to show to others. Before you go public with your act, try changing the position of the two pieces of paper. Move the shorter strip closer and farther from the opening in the longer, folded strip. Set the small strip off to one side a bit. If you want to get really fancy, make the short strip out of dark colored paper. Now, check your illusion.

Climb the Highest Mountain

Draw an outline of three mountains on a 4-inch square of paper. Illus. 67 shows this. Cut along the line. Now, which seems longer, the distance from left to right along the mountains' bases or from top to bottom of the tallest peak? Study your cutout and see for yourself.

Illus. 67

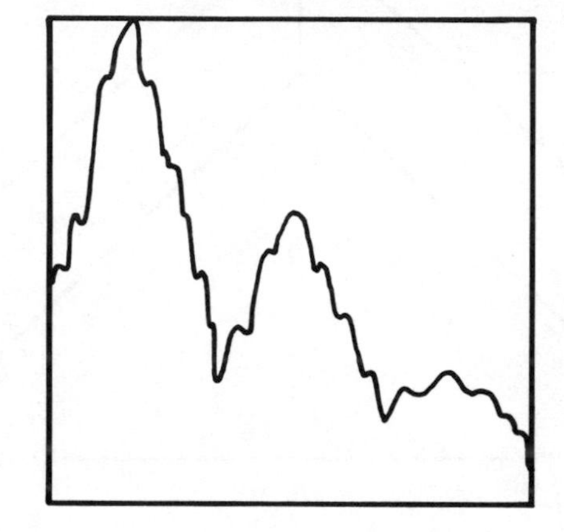

If you want to perform a little experiment, see if it makes any difference if you color the three mountains each a different color.

· 6 ·
Around and Around

Spokes That Aren't There

Take a close look at Illus. 68.

See any spokes?

Now hold the book up and rotate it back and forth looking directly at Illus. 68. Those flickers aren't really flickers, just as those spokes aren't really spokes. Of course, the movement you see is another optical illusion. The reason that it works is that sometimes your mind works faster than your eyes.

Illus. 68

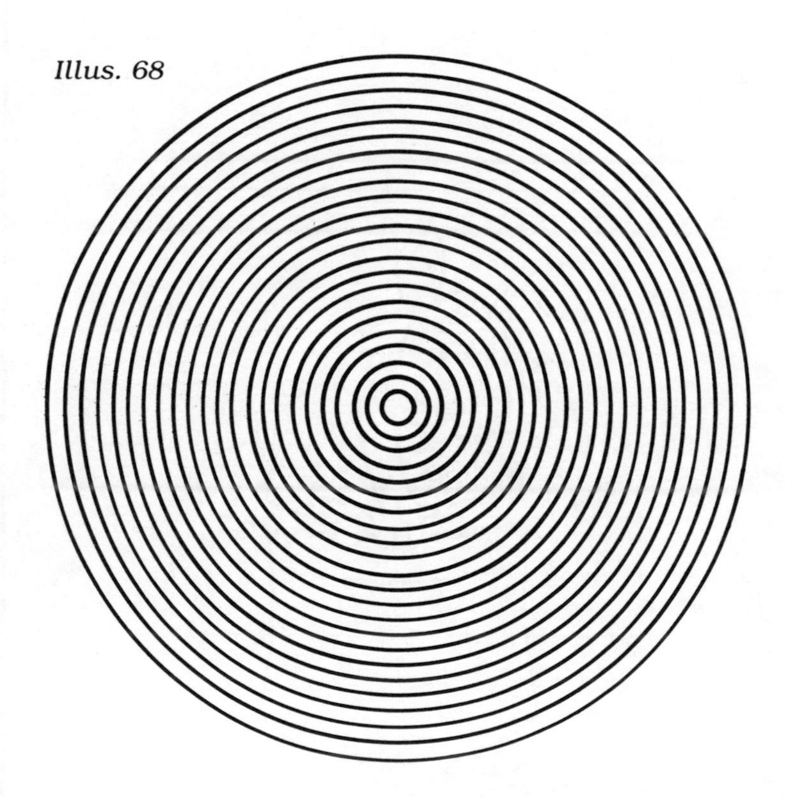

Here's another example: How many times have you seen, on television or in movies, wheels moving faster and faster? At first the spokes are easy to follow. Soon the wagon spokes become a blur; then they start turning backwards, even though they're still moving forward.

The wheels aren't really changing direction. When they reach a certain speed they start to "outrun" your eyes (or the movie film). Illus. 69 shows a turning wheel. Naturally, wheels have more than one spoke, but looking at just one spoke makes it easier to see what happens.

Illus. 69

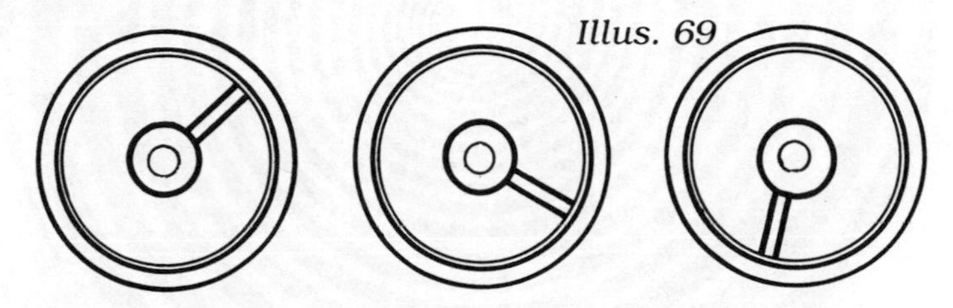

Now, the wheel begins to turn faster, but your eye still takes in pictures at the same speed. Illus. 70 shows the same wheel now turning faster.

Illus. 70

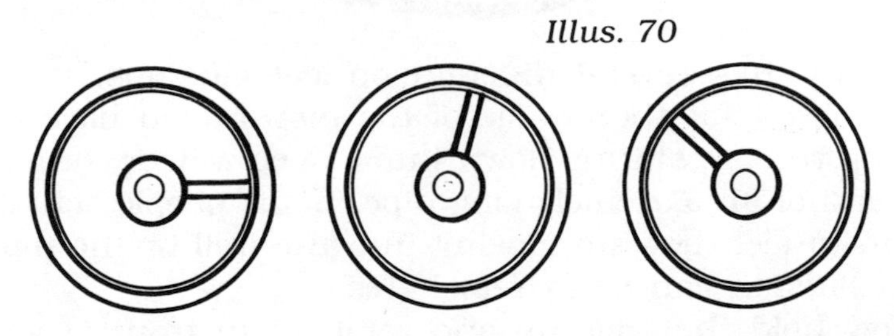

When your eye sends these pictures to your brain, you get the impression the wheel is really turning backwards, even though logic says the wheel is still turning forward. This is because before your eyes can figure out what's happened, your brain has already come to a conclusion, whether it's the spoke turning backwards, or the imaginary spokes in Illus. 70. They appear because your brain can't see all the individual circles at once.

Into the Well

Illus. 71

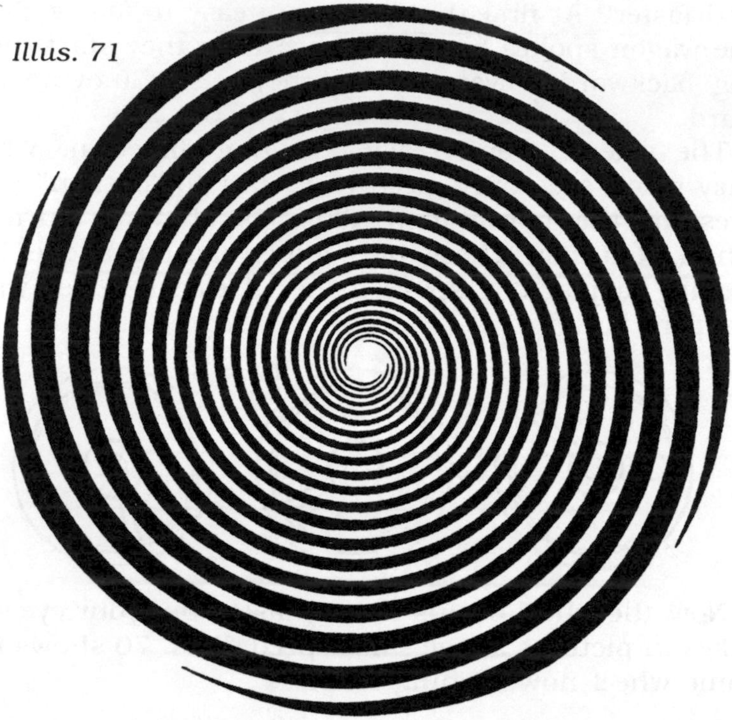

Illus. 71. has several different optical illusions. If you look directly at the middle of the picture you have the feeling you are staring down into a deep well or through the end of an extremely long pipe. Some people actually begin to feel they are moving into the well or the pipe. This illusion can be extremely real.

Now hold the page up and rotate it in front of you. Because the curves are so close together you probably see the same sort of spokes you saw in Illus. 71.

There is still another illusion. Turn the page quickly to the right; then turn it rapidly back to the left. What seems to happen to the size of the drawing? It isn't getting larger or smaller, but because it's really four curved lines, instead of circles, there is the illusion of a change in size.

Circles Inside of Circles

Draw a circle 6 inches or so across. Plain white paper is all right, but something a little stiffer might be better.

Draw the two overlapping circles as shown in Illus. 72. They should be the same size, about 1 inch across. After you draw the circles, go over them with a dark pen or pencil or a marker. They have to be dark so that you can focus on them easily when the whole disc is spinning.

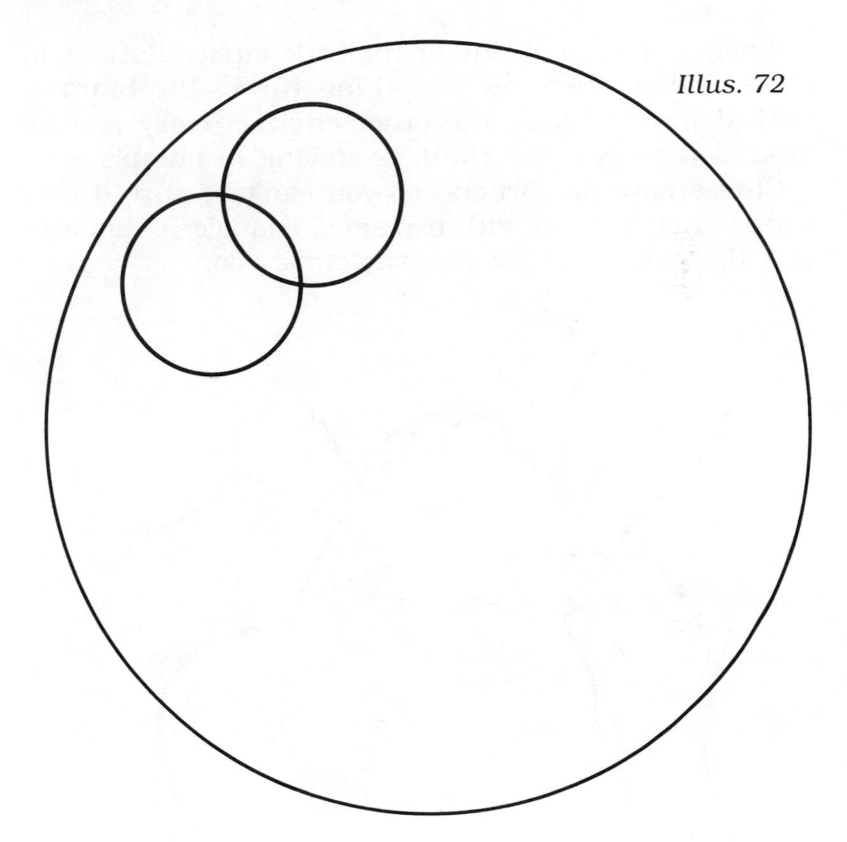

Illus. 72

Cut out the large circle and punch a small hole in its center.

Now spin the disc on the point of a pencil or a pin. Focus on either of the two small circles. What does the circle seem to do as the disc spins? Of course, there is no way for either of those little circles to move except as the larger disc turns. So, why do you see what you seem to see?

If you have a record turntable handy, place the disc on the turntable; then concentrate on watching the little circles.

When you stare at one of the little circles it stays in one position; then, as everything turns, the brain is tricked into thinking the other circle is really moving around the circle you think is staying in one place.

Circles have no corners, so you can't be sure if they turn or not. Try this with two small triangles or squares and they won't behave the way circles do.

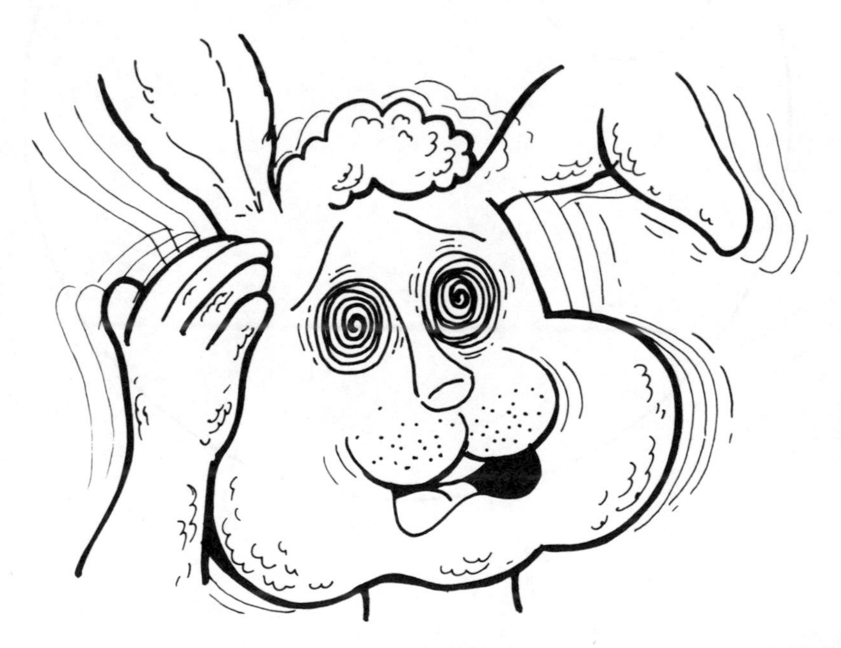

PLEASE, NO MORE CIRCLES!

Those Lines Are Not Circles

This illusion requires some fairly stiff material. Three-by five-inch file cards are perfect. If you only have the 4 × 6-inch cards, cut them in half so that they become 3 × 4-inch cards.

Draw the four lines in Illus. 73 on one of the cards. Make the lines fairly dark so that they are easy to see. Spin the card on a pin or on a pencil point. Be sure to poke the hole in the exact center of the card so that it does not spin off-center.

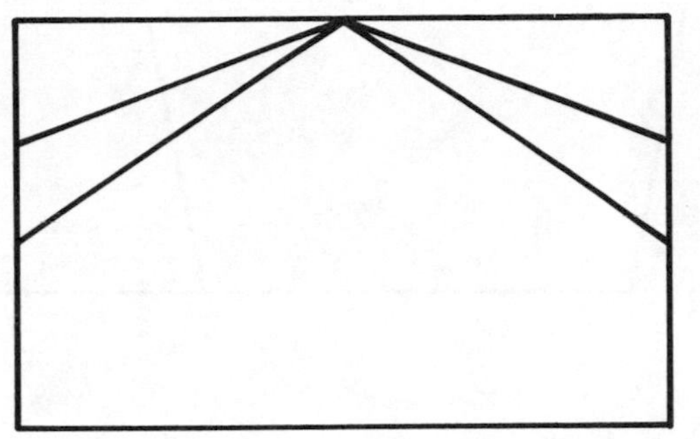

Illus. 73

To find the center of a rectangle, turn the card over, and draw a line from one corner to the opposite corner; then connect the remaining opposite corners. Illus. 74 shows how to do this. Where the two lines cross is the rectangle's center. (This is not an optical illusion!)

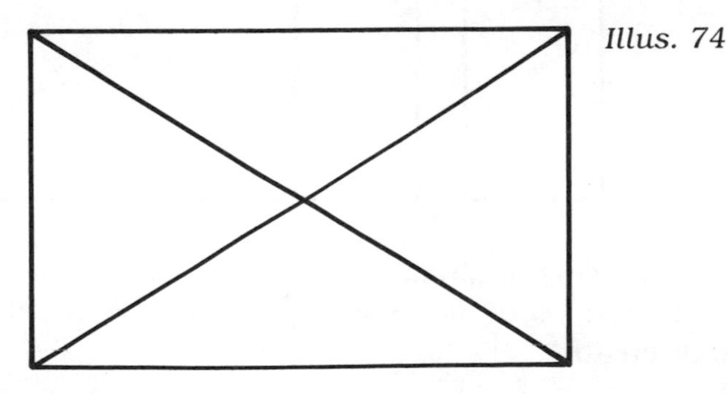

Illus. 74

When you spin the card, something strange happens to the straight lines you drew. Try it and see.

Illus. 75 and Illus. 76 show two more sets of lines for you to draw on fresh cards. Spin each card and see what develops.

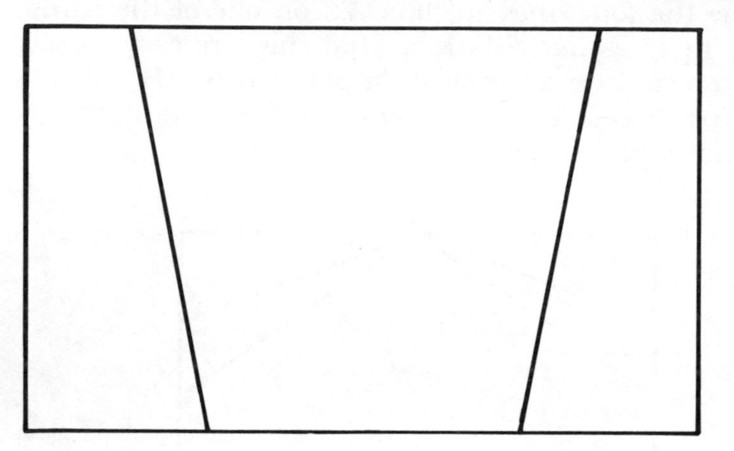

Illus. 75

Illus. 76

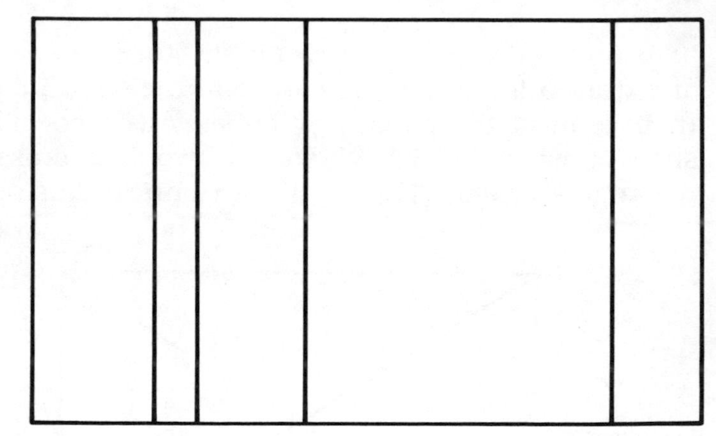

If this sort of illusion fascinates you, try some lines of your own. You never know what sort of illusion you may create.

Spinner

The Spinner is a simple way to make your mind think it is seeing something which is not really there, because the Spinner's two separate pictures move so fast that your mind sees the two images as one.

You need a circle of fairly stiff material. It must be stiffer than a file card because a file card will bend when you try to use it. File folders are fine, but cereal box sides won't work because you need material which is plain on both sides.

If you have to use the cereal box, draw a circle on it, cut it out, and use it to trace another circle on plain paper. Glue the paper onto the colored side of the cardboard and you're set.

If you don't have a pencil compass handy, anything round will do, since any size circle will work unless it is too large or too small to spin or draw on.

In the middle of one side of the cardboard disc draw a fish, as in Illus. 77. Turn the disc over so that the bottom now becomes the top. Do not turn it over from one side to the other. Draw three bubbles rising. Position them so that they would be directly above the fish's mouth if the fish were on this side of the circle. Illus. 78 shows how.

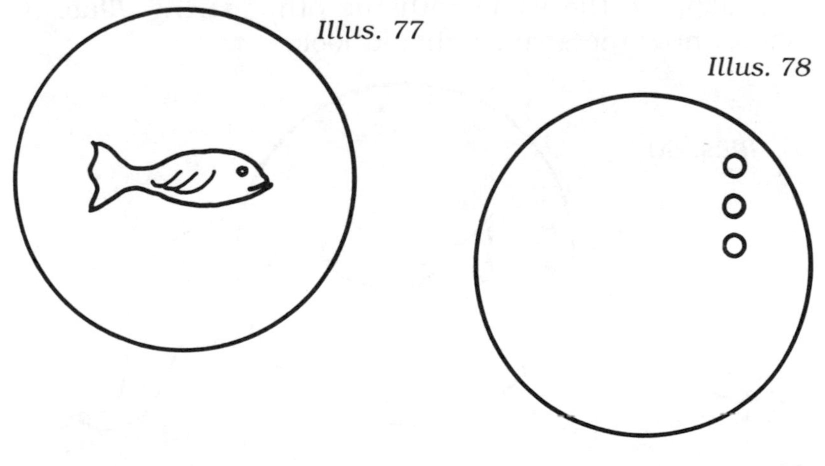

Illus. 77

Illus. 78

You must draw the bubbles in the right location. Take just a second or two and turn the disc over so that you can see exactly where the fish's mouth is before drawing the bubbles.

Once you are sure you have the bubbles in the right position, make both the fish and its bubbles fairly dark. This makes them easier to see when your Spinner does its thing.

Now make two holes on each side of the disc. Illus. 79 shows where to make them. Make them between ½ inch and 1 inch apart, and ¼ inch from the edge of the material.

Illus. 79

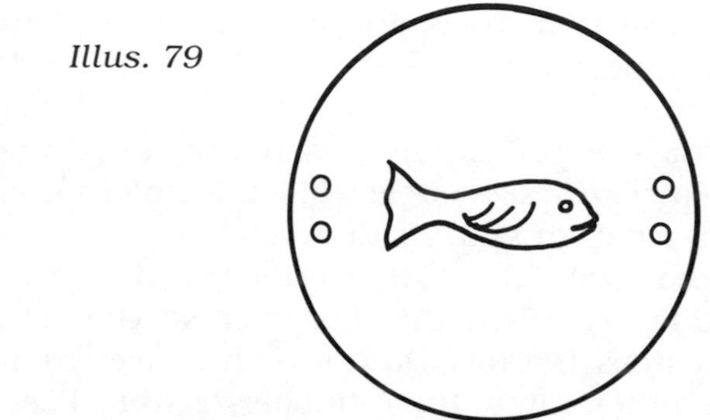

Now cut two pieces of string, each about 1½ feet long. Thread one piece through the two holes on one side of the Spinner and tie its ends together to make a big loop. Do the same with the other string. Illus. 80 shows how the strings should look.

Illus. 80

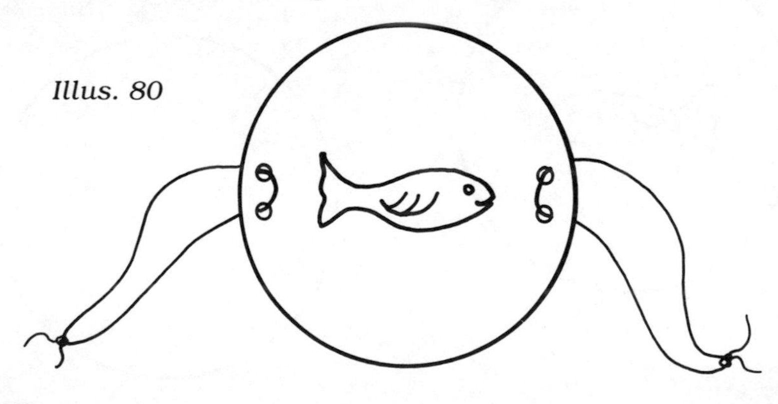

Hold one string in each hand and spin the cardboard around and around until the strings are twisted. Pull your hands apart so that the Spinner turns rapidly and look directly at it as it spins. You will see the bubbles rising from the fish's mouth.

Looks OK to me!

Of course, this is an optical illusion. But it is the sort of illusion which has fascinated people for many years.

Here are some more ideas: Draw several fish on one side of the disc and put their fish tank on the other side. Try putting a bird on one side and its cage on the other side. Draw the head of a criminal and put the jail bars on the opposite side of the disc. Put a ballplayer on one side and have him or her ready to kick the ball on the other. Use stick figures if you want.

Just for the fun of it make another disc. Color one side yellow and the other side blue. When this disc spins rapidly, your mind should tell you the disc looks more green than yellow or blue.

Over and Over

This is a variation of the Spinner. It is easier to use once you have constructed the basic system.

To begin this project, you need a piece of cardboard such as the side of an empty cereal box. Cut a piece about 3½ inches wide and about 8 inches long from the front or back of the box. Fold it into two sections, each 4 inches high. Unfold the cardboard so that it looks like Illus. 81.

Place a turning rod inside the cardboard. A long pencil will do just fine, but so will a long piece of dowel rod. A dowel rod, in case you did not know, is a long, round piece of wood.

Tape the turning rod securely onto one side of the cardboard, as in Illus. 82.

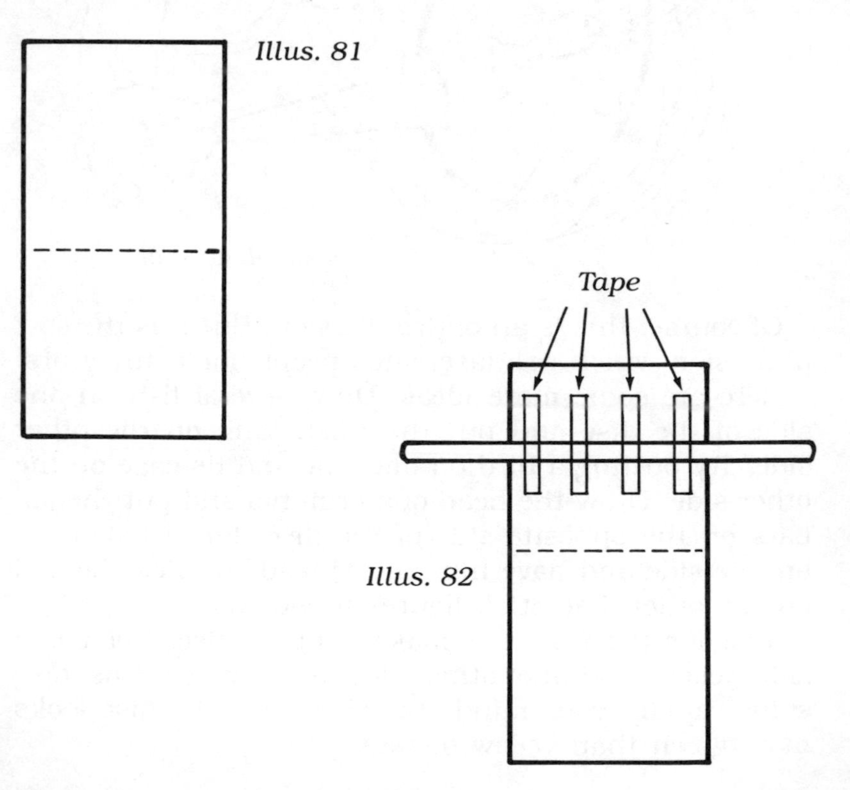

Illus. 81

Illus. 82

Refold the cardboard and tape the loose ends together. Illus. 83 shows your project at this stage.

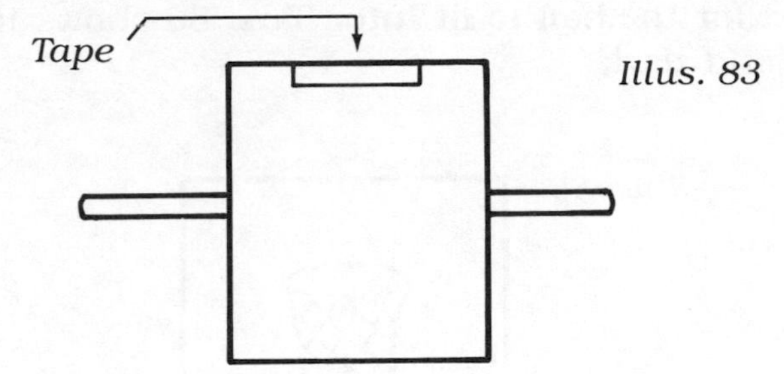

Illus. 83

Cut a strip of plain white paper 9 inches long and as wide as the piece of cardboard. Fold this strip of paper around the outside of the turning base. It should fit just loosely enough so that you can slip the paper off the base. Tape the loose flap down as in Illus. 84.

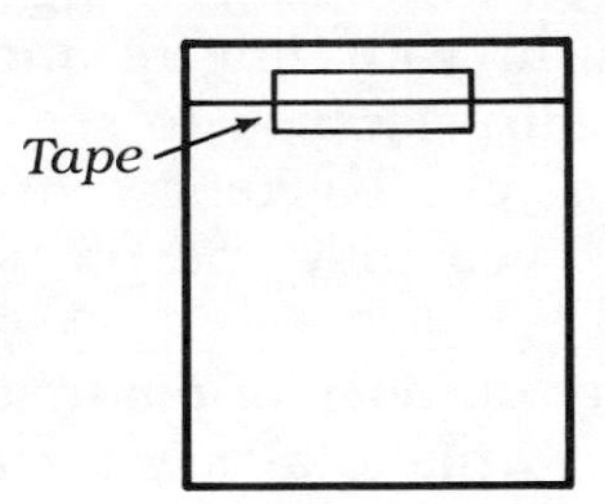

Illus. 84

Once the flap is taped, slip the paper off the turning base. For your first illusion, draw a ball on one side of the paper, as in Illus. 85. Make it good and dark so that it is easy to see when things are spinning around and around.

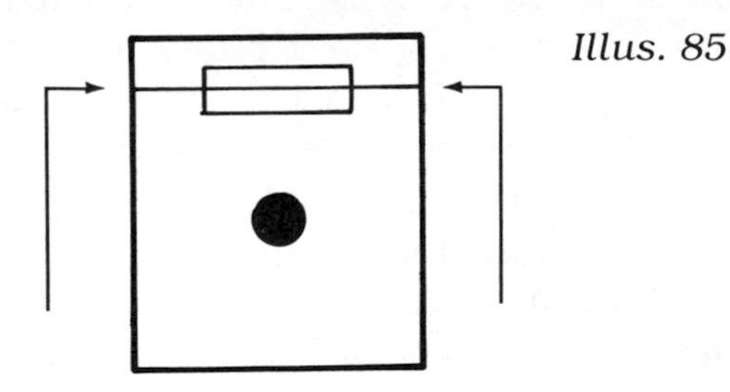
Illus. 85

Turn the folded paper over from top to bottom. Follow the arrows in Illus. 85 when you turn the paper. Draw a basket for the ball to fit into. Illus. 86 shows it. Make it good and dark.

Illus. 86

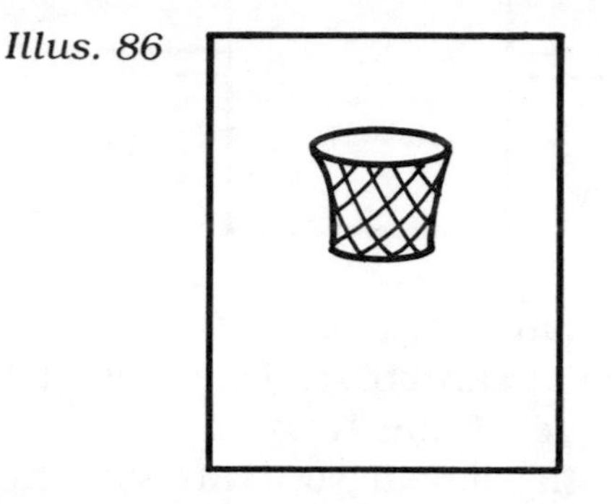

Slip the paper back over the turning base. Spin the turning rod rapidly in your fingers and focus on the ball. It should not surprise you to see the ball in the basket. Of course, if your basket is not lined up properly in the drawing, you may end up with a rim shot instead of a basket.

You can make any number of pictures for this great toy without having to make a new turning base. Just cut another strip of paper, fold and tape it, draw the pictures, and slip the paper onto the base.

How about having a fish on one side and a worm on the other? Or maybe a bat and a ball, a tennis racket and a ball, an arrow and a target, etc. Just make sure to get your two drawings lined up correctly.

If you want to be a little fancier with your Over and Over illusion, make a holder for the turning base; then you can concentrate on the picture while spinning just one end of the turning rod. A cereal box or some similar box is the best material. Fold a piece of lightweight cardboard so that it looks like a big U as in Illus. 87. Be sure the bottom of the U is wide enough for your turning base to fit between the cardboard sides.

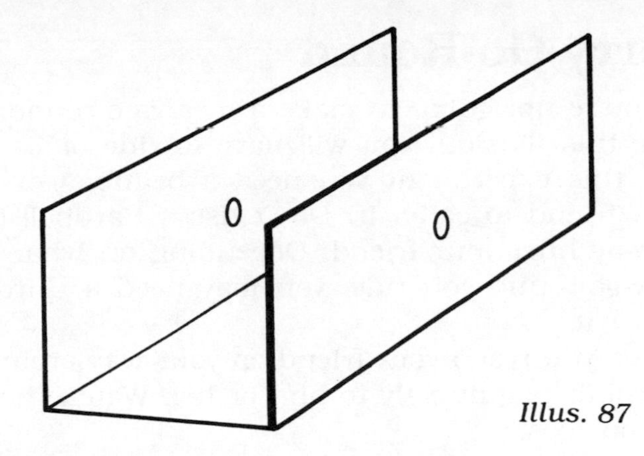

Illus. 87

Poke two holes in the sides of the cardboard as in Illus. 87. Make them large enough so that the pencil or turning rod can fit through them and turn easily. Just be sure you put the holes in the cardboard and not in your finger!

Insert Over and Over into your holder so that it looks like Illus. 88.

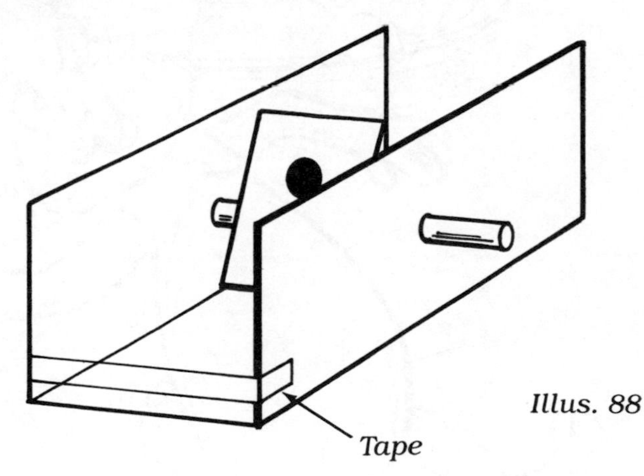

Illus. 88

Use a piece of tape to hold the sides of the frame together while you spin the turning rod. Illus. 88 shows this. Put the tape near the bottom so that you can spread the top of the frame apart and get the rod in and out each time you use a new picture.

Merry-Go-Round

No, you're not going to make a merry-go-round, but to create this illusion, you will have to ride one.

For this experiment you need a beanbag or softball and a friend to catch it. Don't use a hardball because you may hurt your friend. Depending on what kind of merry-go-round you ride, you may need a third friend to turn it.

When you reach your friend on your way around, toss the ball or bag directly to him or her. Watch the ball or bag you toss.

Wait until you get to the park to try this illusion; then decide for yourself whether the ball you toss really curves or whether this, too, is just another moving optical illusion.

I think you threw it a little soon!

• 7 •
Making Pictures Move

Quick Flip

Before movies, television, and VCR's were a part of daily life, people had to use other things to make pictures move. No one knows who discovered how to make drawings move, but grandparents and great-grandparents probably experimented with the illusions in this chapter.

These ways of making pictures move are just as much fun today as they were years and years ago.

Cut a 3-inch-wide strip of notebook paper from the long side of a sheet of paper. This gives you a strip of paper 3 inches wide and 11 or so inches long. Fold it in half the long way so that it looks like Illus. 89.

Illus. 89

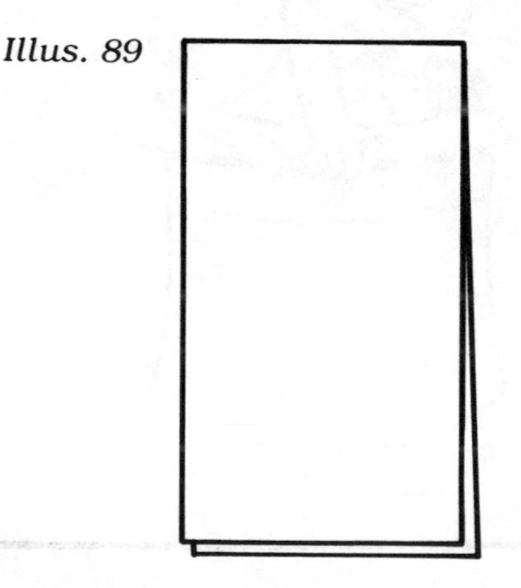

Next, draw a figure in the lower half of the top layer of paper. A stick figure is fine. Illus. 90 shows one doing a jumping jack.

Illus. 90

Lift the top sheet and draw a second figure on the bottom sheet. Put this figure in a little different position than thc one on the top sheet. In Illus. 91, the figure is in a different part of the exercise.

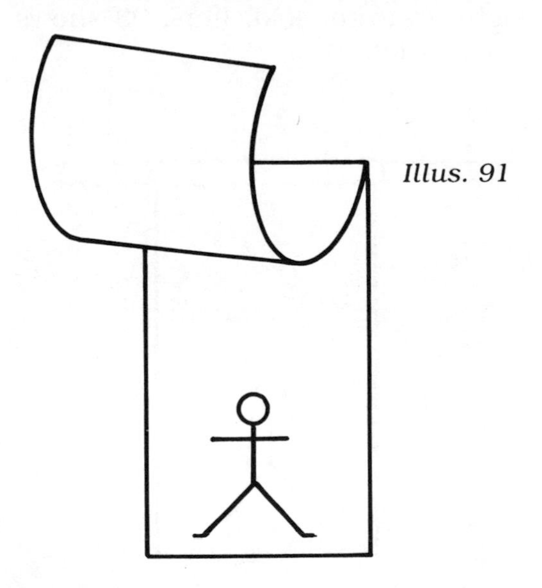

Illus. 91

Line up the second figure right below the first. This is easy to do, since you made faint creases in the second sheet when you drew the first figure.

Now return the Quick Flip to its folded position and place a pencil at the bottom of the top page, as in Illus. 92.

Illus. 92

Roll just the top sheet around the pencil as tightly as possible, right up to the fold. Illus. 93 shows what your Quick Flip looks like now.

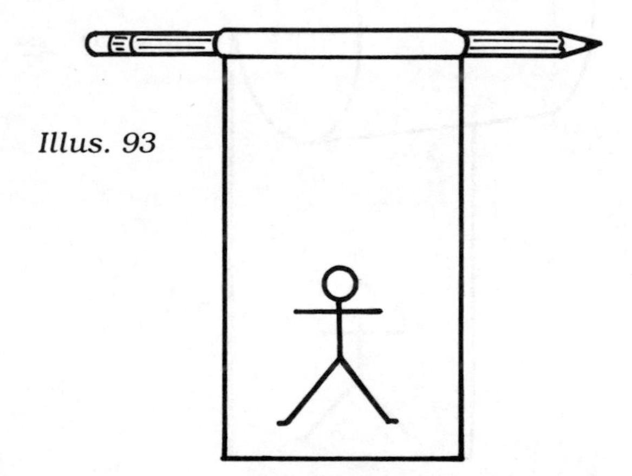

Illus. 93

Pull the pencil out of the roll. The tightly rolled paper will unroll just a bit. Unroll the paper all the way, and let go of it. As soon as you do, the page will spring back into a little roll. This is what you want.

Hold the bottom sheet with one hand, and the pencil with the other. Use the eraser end of the pencil to pull the rolled paper down flat. Slide the pencil towards the fold about halfway. This will let the top sheet of paper spring up. Quickly move the pencil back down towards the bottom of the page and move it back and forth. Illus. 94 shows the Quick Flip in action.

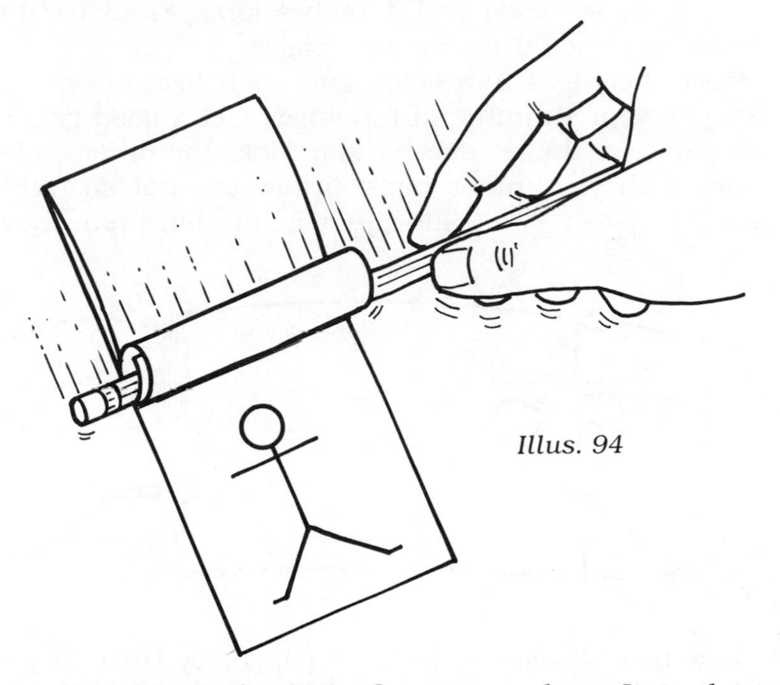

Illus. 94

Look right at the little figure you drew. It is doing jumping jacks! The faster you move the top sheet, the faster the figure moves back and forth.

When the jumping jacks get dull, you could have a player bounce a ball, a dog chase a ball, let someone catch a fish, or draw a person moving a box from one place to another. Make a bunch of these clever little moving optical illusions.

Flipper

Your parents or grandparents probably got flip books as prizes in cereal boxes when they were children. You may even have seen some yourself. A Flipper shows an action taking place.

The first step is to make a flipper pad, which is really nothing more than a pad of paper. You could buy a pad of paper or use up the ones around the house, but it's more fun to make a flipper pad.

Cut two sheets of notebook or typing paper into sections 2 inches wide and 4 inches long. From the two sheets you should get sixteen pages.

Place the pages in a stack and hold them at one end between your thumb and forefinger. Get a good grip on the paper so that it doesn't slip. Hold the other end of pages with your other hand firmly, but not so tightly that the paper can't slide just a bit. Illus. 95 shows how.

Illus. 95

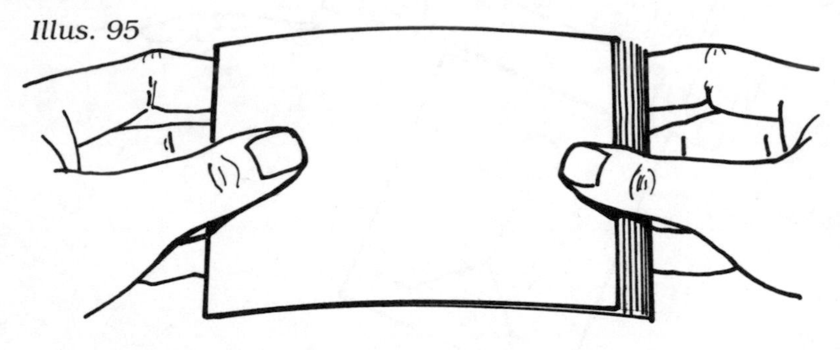

Now bend back the stack of papers by turning your first hand. As you do this, the papers will all shift just a tiny bit. If you are turning your left hand you will see the edges of the sheets appear in your right hand. When this happens, tighten your right hand and relax the left.

The edges of the pad now slope from top to bottom. Put a staple in the pad as shown in Illus. 96 and your Flipper is ready for some serious drawing.

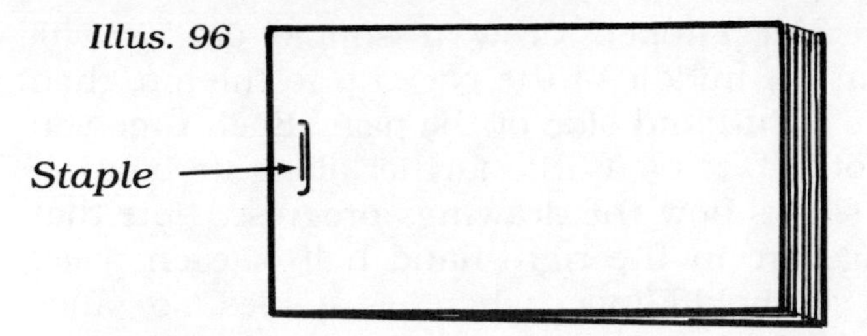

Now make a series of drawings, one on each sheet, which are very much alike, so that each drawing changes slightly from the one before. This change shows the movement. In fact, this is the way cartoons were originally made. Thousands and thousands of drawings were photographed, and as the pictures ran through a projector, the characters moved.

Eh, is this how Bugs Bunny got started?

For your first Flipper, draw a simple dot. It will bounce from the middle of the page up to the top, then down to the right-hand side of the page. Each time you draw the dot, it will be a little farther along its bounce.

Illus. 97 shows how the drawings progress. Note that the drawings are in the right-hand half of each page. Remember, you hold Flipper where it's stapled, so, since it's stapled on the left, anything drawn on the left won't be seen.

Illus. 97

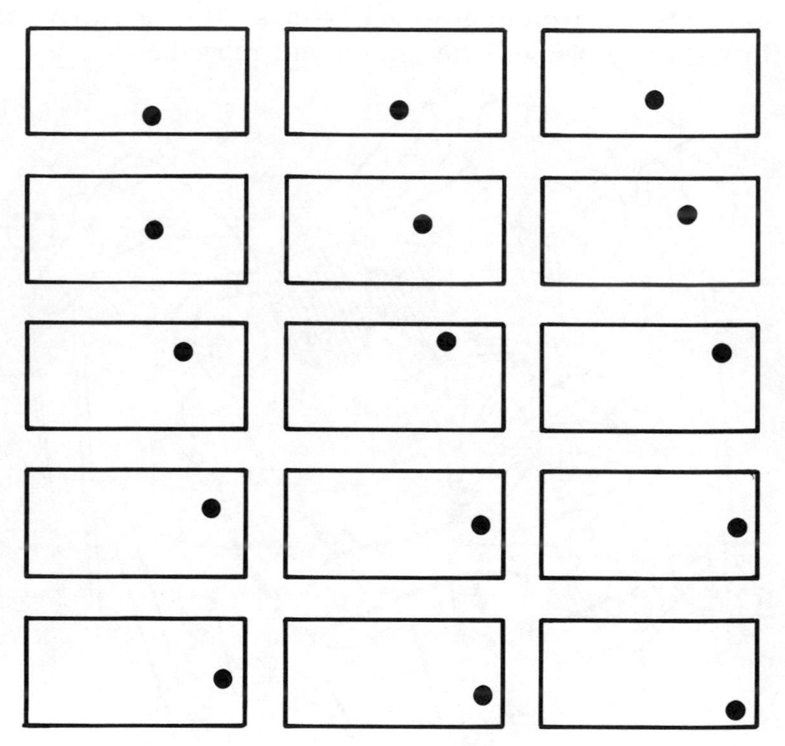

Hold the Flipper in your left hand over the stapled part. Put your right hand over the edges of the pages on the right. Bend your left hand back a bit and let the ends of the pages slip past your right thumb. Illus. 98 shows this.

Illus. 98

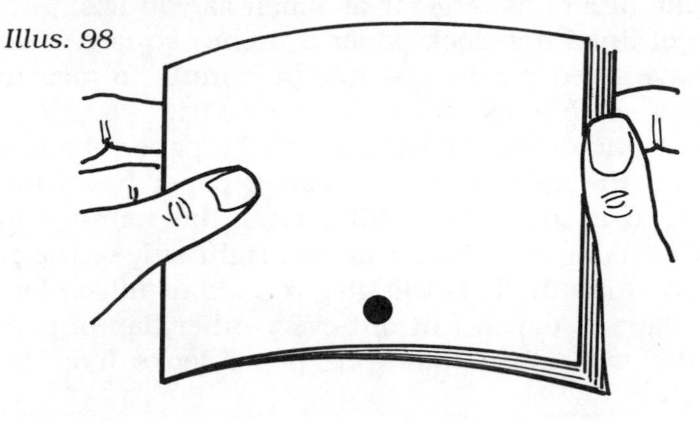

Stare directly at the ball and watch it bounce from the bottom of the page to the top. The faster you flip the pages, the faster the ball bounces.

Here is a tip. The closer one drawing is to the next, the smoother the action is. Also, the more pages there are in your Flipper, the more action you can give your ball or whatever. You can make Flippers of as many pages as you want to draw or as many as you can staple.

Get a little fancier and have a fish swim up and down or do a loop. Let it blow bubbles as it swims. Think about using stick figures which walk, run, or jump. Have them do some jumping jacks or other exercises such as push-ups. If you work from the back of the Flipper to the front, you can see the previous drawing through the paper each time you let a clean sheet flip down. That way you know exactly where to place your next figure.

You can also try making a Flipper in the opposite direction. Just bend the sheets the other way before you staple the pad together.

Come and Go

Come and Go takes a bit of time to prepare, but once made can be used again and again.

Make your first Come and Go fairly small (later, you can make others as large or as small as you wish). Cut a piece of lined notebook paper 5 inches square. If you don't have lined paper, just take a minute to measure and draw some lines about ⅜ inch apart.

Draw a line down the left side of the paper about an inch from the side (if your notebook paper has a margin line, use that). Illus. 99 shows the margin and lines. Cut along each line from the right side of the paper to the margin. This will give you about fifteen long, skinny flaps of paper. Cut out every other flap of paper along the margin so that your paper looks like Illus. 100.

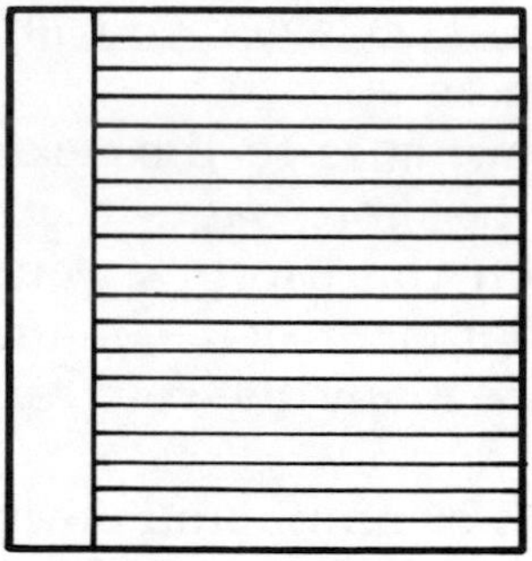

Illus. 99

Illus. 100

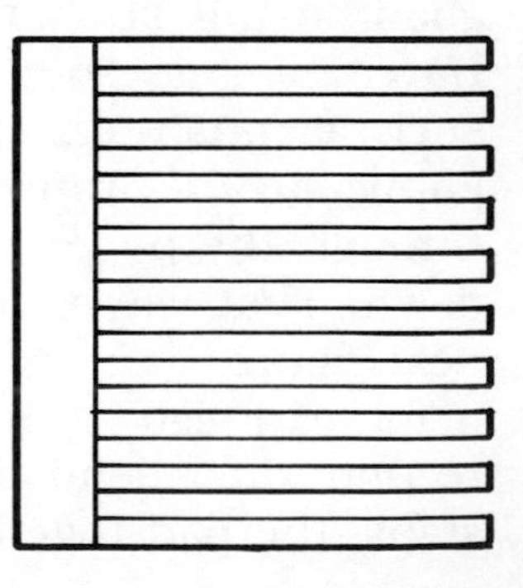

Place the long edge of a 3 × 5-inch file card or piece of cardboard on the margin of the paper. Fold that margin over and tape it down on the back of the cardboard, as in Illus. 101. Fold the loose ends over and tape them down as well.

Keep these two hints in mind. Make certain you keep the loose ends the same distance apart, and fold and tape only two or three of the ends at a time. Illus. 101 shows the Come and Go with the ends all taped down.

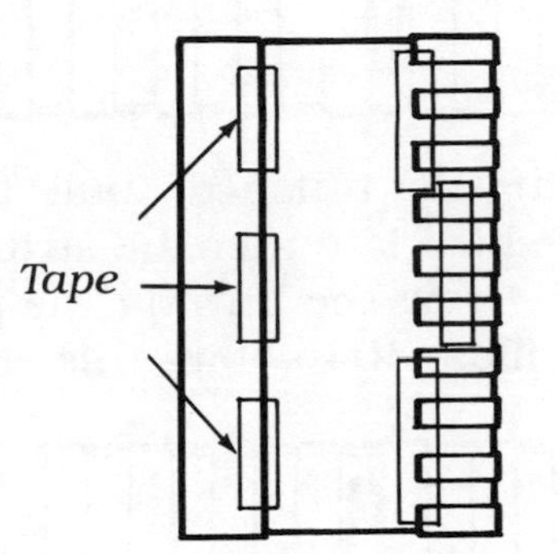

Illus. 101

Turn the viewing frame over so that the taped part is on the back. Cut a piece of paper 6 inches long and just a fraction less than 3 inches wide. Slip it into the viewing frame so that it slides on top of the cardboard and under the strips of paper, as in Illus. 102.

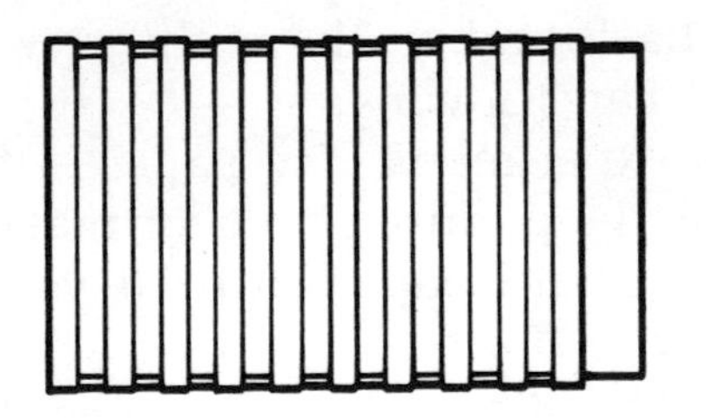

Illus. 102

Now begin drawing your picture. Only draw on the piece of paper you just slipped into the viewing frame. Do not draw on the viewing frame itself, or Come and Go won't work.

Start with a bird with its wings outstretched, as in Illus. 103.

Illus. 103

After the drawing is finished, pull the paper far enough so that the bird is under the strips, and all you see is blank paper. Draw the bird on the paper with its wings down a bit. Illus. 104 shows this step completed.

Illus. 104

To make the bird move, just slide the strip of paper back and forth in the viewing frame. First, you see the bird with its wings either up or down; the next instant, the wings have changed position. Move the picture strip rapidly back and forth in the viewing frame and your bird will flap its wings.

Feel free to experiment. Try paper stiffer than notebook paper for the picture sheet, or make a larger viewing frame using stiff paper. Turn it vertically and use the paper up and down.

Here are a few ideas for other pictures: a chicken picking up grain; maybe a rabbit hopping and flopping its ears; a person sawing wood or just walking; or a ball player swinging a bat or throwing a ball.

Spinning Viewer

This project takes a few minutes to construct but is so different from what most of us have seen it is well worth the effort.

Make a circle about 8 inches across on a sheet of cardboard. A flattened-out large cereal box is perfect. Corrugated cardboard from a supermarket carton is good, but since the cereal box is easier to cut and fold, you might be better off with the lighter cardboard if it is available.

Add four prongs to the drawing, as in Illus. 105. This is the base for your viewer.

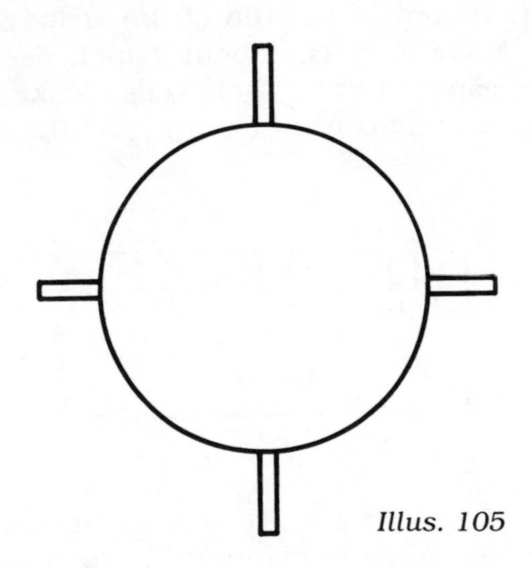

Illus. 105

Cut the base out and fold the four prongs up so that they are at right angles to the base. Make sure each fold is right along the edge of the circle. If you use heavy cardboard, it is a good idea to score the material before making the folds.

Cut two sheets of stiff paper in half the long way. Construction paper is good. If you don't have stiff paper, glue or tape two pieces of notebook or typing paper together. Take three of these strips (they should be 4 × 11 inches) and tape them together so that the long strip looks like Illus. 106.

Illus. 106

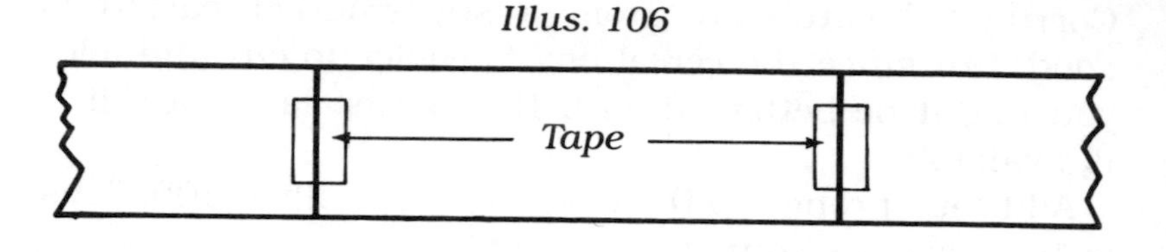

Cut sections out of the top of the strip as shown in Illus. 107. Make each cut about 1 inch deep from the top of the paper, and ¼ inch wide. Make these cuts every 2 inches, and continue cutting all the way around the strip.

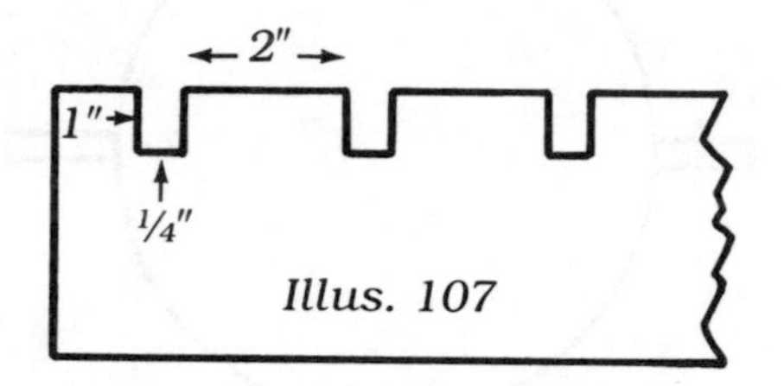

Illus. 107

Form the strip into a circle and slip it onto the cardboard base inside the four prongs. Make sure the paper completely fills the outer edge of the base. The ends of the strip will probably overlap a bit. Mark the point at which the extra end overlaps, and leave 1 inch extra. Cut off the rest. Illus. 108 shows how.

If your cardboard circle is a little larger than the paper, just add the fourth strip of stiff paper to it, and measure it the same way. Just make sure to add any ¼-inch cuts that are needed.

Illus. 108

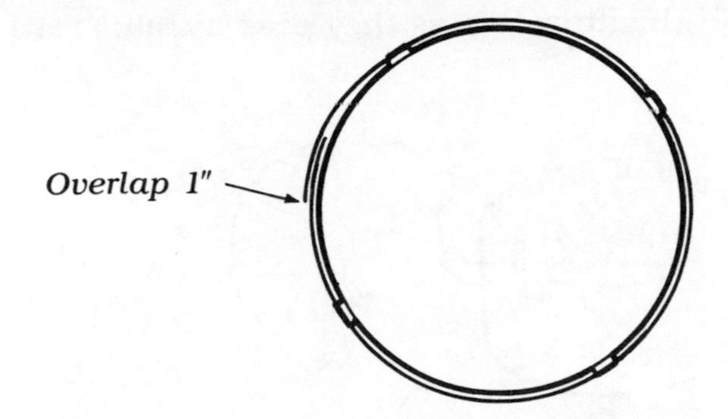

Once the paper has been measured and cut, spread it flat before you. In the 2 inches between each cut, draw one scene of a moving picture. Illus. 109 shows a rabbit with extremely active ears. This is a good subject for your first Spinning Viewer. Make the rabbit sit right at the bottom of the paper and keep it just below the cuts you just made in the top of the paper strip. Position each drawing between a pair of cuts.

Illus. 109

Once you have drawn your way around the paper strip it is show time. Form the strip back into a circle and tape the loose ends of the strip together. Set the strip on the base and tape the four cardboard prongs to the picture strip.

If you have a record turntable, poke a hole in the exact center of the base just enough to fit over the turntable's spindle. Set the viewer on the turntable and start it.

Look through the little slits as they pass by. Illus. 110 shows how.

Illus. 110

Look across and down and focus on the little rabbits as they go by.

If you don't have a turntable to use, then stick a thumbtack through the center of the base. Push the tack's point into the eraser on a pencil, as in Illus. 111.

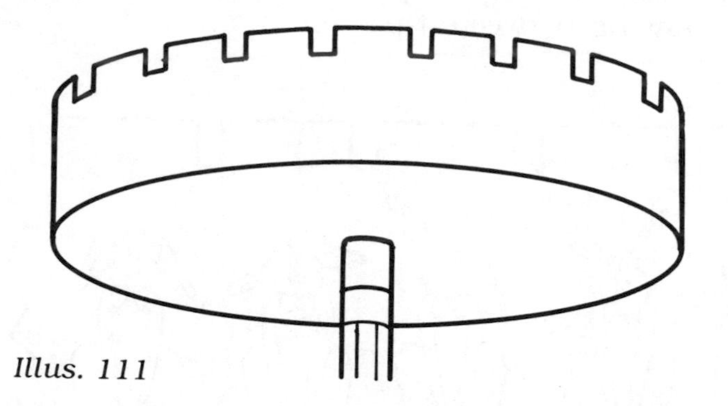

Illus. 111

Hold the pencil between both sets of fingers and thumbs and twirl it. Look through the slits just as though the viewer was set up on a turntable. It is not quite as fancy as a turntable but works just fine.

When you want to make another set of drawings, do not go through all the cutting you did the first time. Just cut the paper strips about 3 inches wide, and tape them together and cut off any extra paper as you did before. Draw the pictures (space them 2½ inches apart) and just slip this strip inside the viewer.

8 Seeing Isn't Believing

Dangerous Curves

By now it comes as no surprise to you that the old expression "Seeing is believing" does not always hold true. Here are some great illusions which not only change as we work with them, but may seem to move even as they stand still.

Everyone can tell a curved line from a straight line, but by the time you finish this project you may wonder whether a curved line is a straight one.

Draw a square on a piece of paper. For your first project make the square fairly small. A 1-inch square is fine.

Draw the line in Illus. 112. Start it in the upper left-hand corner of the square, and bring it 1⁄16 inch from the upper right-hand corner of the square.

The next line begins as shown in Illus. 113. It runs from the corner formed by the first line and the right-hand edge of the square to the bottom of the square, again about 1⁄16 inch from the right side of the square when the line reaches the bottom.

Illus. 114 shows the next line. It begins in the corner and ends 1⁄16 inch from the lower side of the square, like the others.

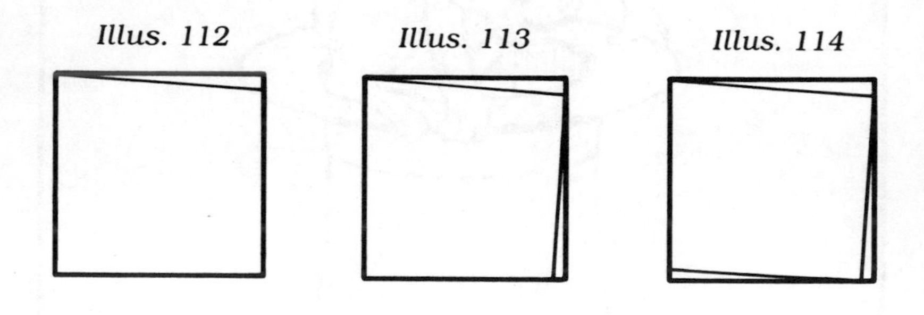

Illus. 112 *Illus. 113* *Illus. 114*

You should have the idea by now. Continue making the lines around the square. Each line begins in the corner and ends 1/16 inch from the line which is already in place.

Illus. 115 shows the next few lines. Notice that each line ends when it meets the line it would cross. Do not cross any lines.

Illus. 115

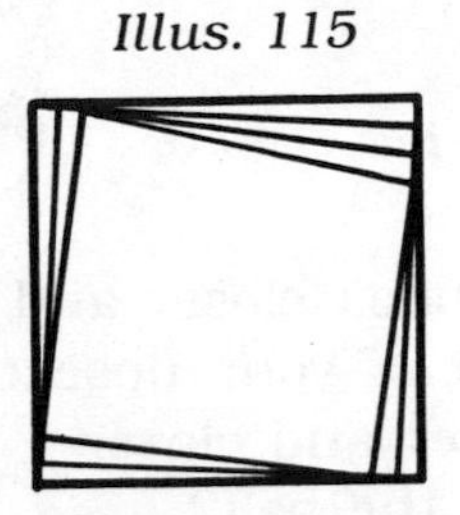

Continue drawing these lines, going around and around the square. Each set of lines should be a bit shorter than the one before. After a few more lines you will also notice something else.

Right before your eyes your straight lines are beginning to form curves. Or are those curves just illusions?

When you have filled the entire square, you have done what seemed impossible. You've made curves appear with just straight lines.

This makes a great art project. Illus. 116 shows other shapes you can experiment with. You could combine several squares or triangles to create some really special illusions.

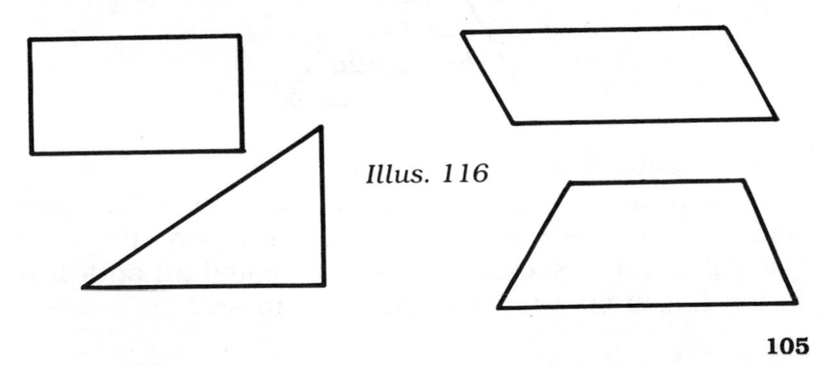

Illus. 116

Two Points

Focus right on the dot between the ball and the hoop in Illus. 117.

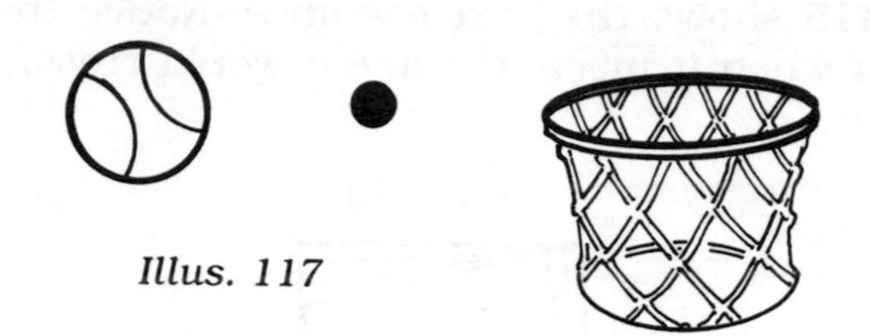

Illus. 117

Slowly move the book closer and closer towards your face. Aim the point of your nose right at the dot and move the book closer and closer.

What happens to the ball?

Make some of these drawings with your friends. Just make sure the inner edge of each object is only about ½ inch from the dot. Put a rabbit in a cage, money into a hand, or something of the sort.

All in the Family

Take a quick look at this:

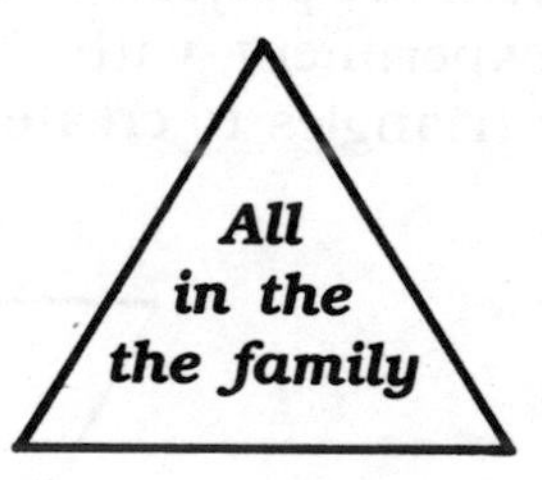

Look again. Count the words.

Something strange happened. You see what your mind wants to see. But after you look again and count the words you discover your mind created an optical illusion based on what you expected to see.

Make Your Own Money

Hold two large coins between your thumb and two fingers as shown in Illus. 118.

Illus. 118

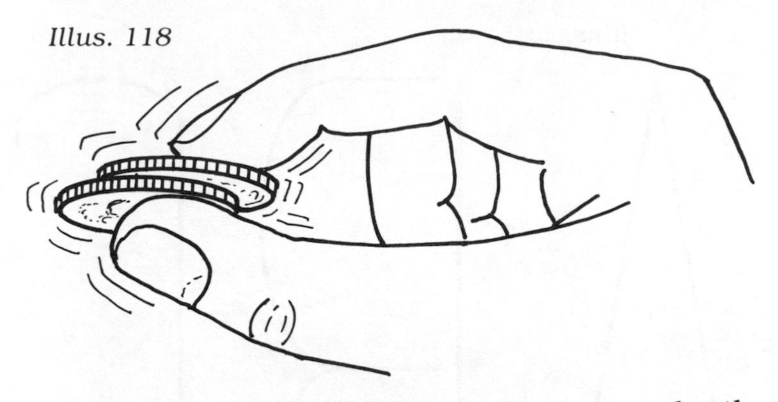

Rub the two coins back and forth against each other. The arrows in Illus. 118 tell you the direction.

Rub the coins faster and faster, and look directly at them as they move back and forth. Where did that third coin come from?

This is another case of afterimage. Your eyes and mind think they are seeing something that has already moved to a new position.

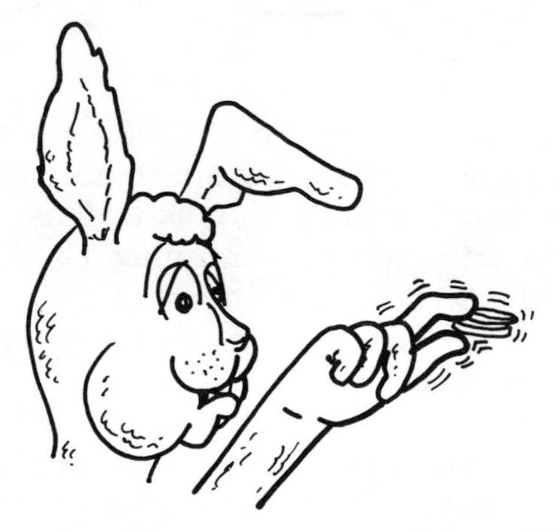

I thought it would make me rich!

Starting the Alphabet

Everyone knows how to begin the alphabet, so Illus. 119 should look familiar to you.

Illus. 119

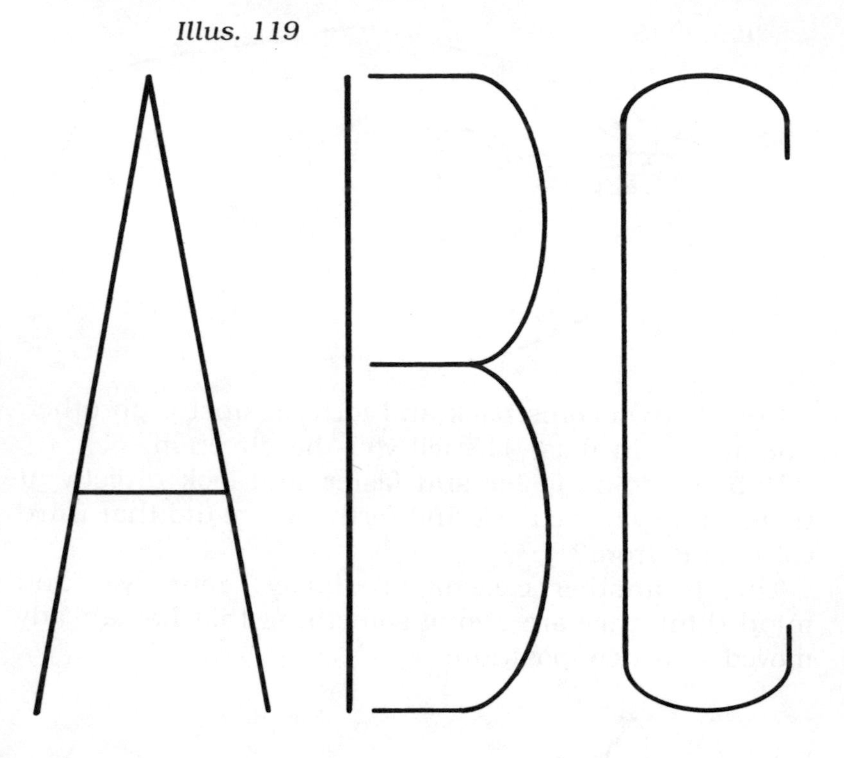

Trace the second letter from the illustration onto a piece of scrap paper. Leave some space on either side of the letter, and copy it exactly as it is in Illus. 119. Now, to the left of the letter write the number 12; then on the right of the letter write the number 14.

Take a look at the three things you just wrote. What has the letter become?

This is another case in which an optical illusion becomes what you expect to see in a certain place. When circumstances change, what you expect to see changes as well.

Finger Touch

You know people need both eyes to see properly. Each eye sees things slightly differently and this different look gives us depth perception. Depth perception tells you how thick things are and how far from the viewer an object is.

Check your depth perception. Close one eye. Hold both hands out in front of you, about 3 feet apart. Extend the index finger of one hand and the little finger of the other hand as in Illus. 120.

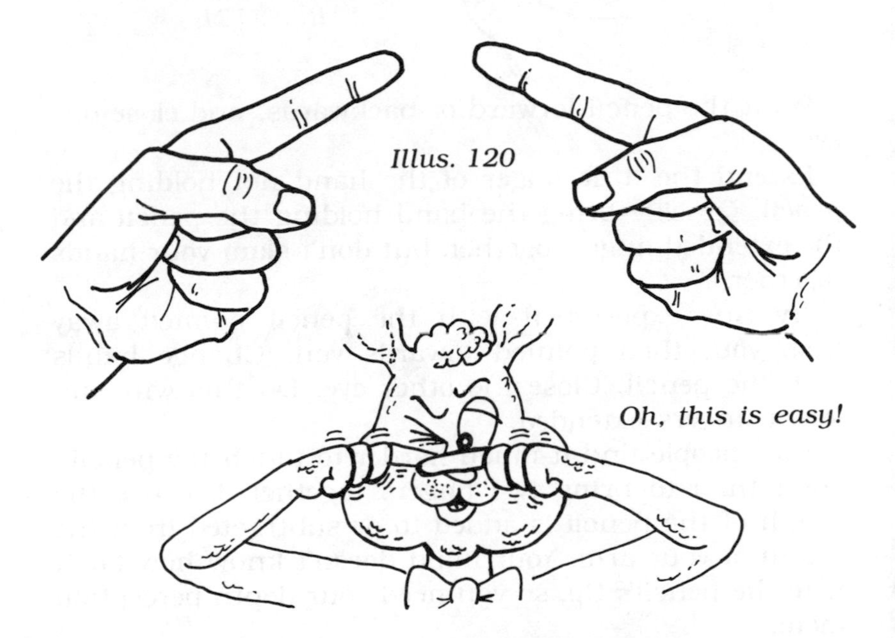

Illus. 120

Oh, this is easy!

Quickly bring your two hands together so that the tips of your two extended fingers just touch. Try this experiment with the other eye closed; then try with different fingers extended. It's tough, because your depth perception is limited when you see with only one eye. However, your body knows how long your arms are; so, you can still come very close to having your fingertips meet.

Get the Point

Let's try another quick experiment in depth perception. Hold a pencil out in front of you in one hand as in Illus. 121.

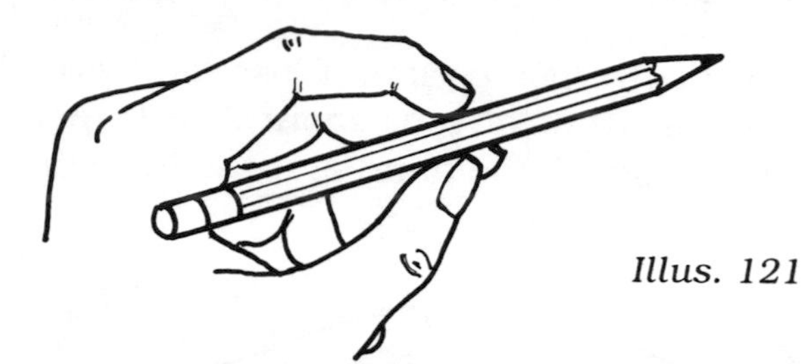

Illus. 121

Point the pencil forward or backwards, and close one eye.

Extend the little finger of the hand not holding the pencil. Quickly bring the hand holding the pencil and the extended finger together, but don't slam your hands together.

Try this experiment with the pencil pointed away from you, then pointed towards you. Change hands with the pencil. Close the other eye. Do this with different fingers extended.

Most people find it much harder to touch the pencil's point than to bring two fingers together, because the length of the pencil is added to or subtracted from the length of your arm. Your mind doesn't know how far it is to the pencil's tip, so you need your depth perception more.

If you study your extended finger and the pencil tip when they are close together, you may experience an optical illusion that makes it seem that one or the other is nearer you, but when you open both eyes you find it is just the opposite.

Try this illusion with your friends. Have a friend close one eye while you walk a few feet away and hold the pencil; then have your friend come up to you with one finger extended and touch the pencil point.

Where's the String?

This depth perception illusion is lots of fun, either alone or with other people. In fact, it works best if someone else sets it up for you.

Fasten a piece of string about at eye level. Taping it to a doorway (as in Illus. 122) is a good way to do this. Cross the room and close one eye. Hold either hand out in front of you with one finger extended. Walk quickly towards the string and touch it with the tip of your extended finger.

Since you have a pretty good idea exactly how far you are from the doorway, you may be able to do this without too much trouble. For a bigger challenge, have a couple of friends hold the string after they have walked across the room or out the door, or have one friend hold the string out in front of himself or herself. Now see how difficult it is to walk towards that string with one eye closed and touch it with the tip of your finger.

After you have done this a few times, try it with a piece of thread. Since the thread is smaller than the string it will be even harder to touch with your fingertip than was the string.

Illus. 122

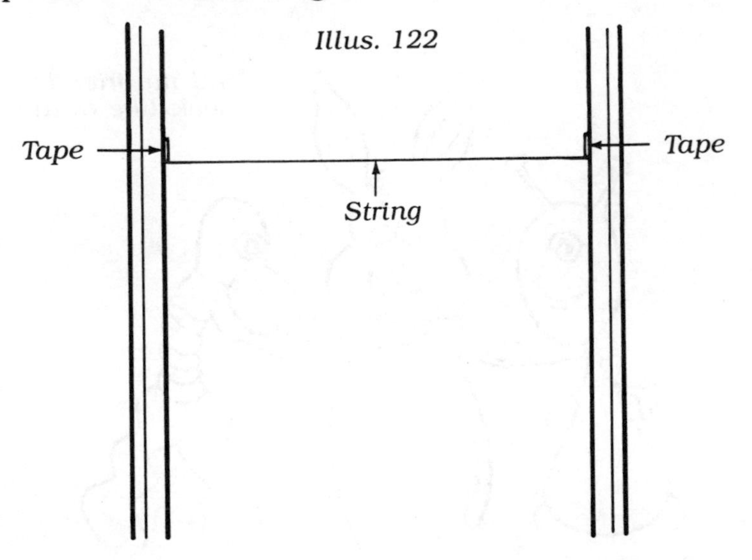

One-Eyed Friend

When you were young you probably did this without realizing it's an optical illusion. For this you need a good friend. He or she must be a good friend because you're going to end up nose to nose—if nobody's around, try it in a mirror.

Face each other and move towards each other until your noses almost touch as in Illus. 123.

Illus. 123

Your friend suddenly has only one eye right in the middle of his or her forehead.

Inside Out or Outside In

A number of optical illusions appear to move or even turn themselves inside out while you are looking at them. Take Illus. 124, for example. Think of it as a folded sheet of paper. Is the fold closer or farther away than the edges of the paper?

Illus. 124

Stare at the drawing for a few seconds and watch the middle of the "folded page" as it moves nearer to you and farther away than the edges of the paper.

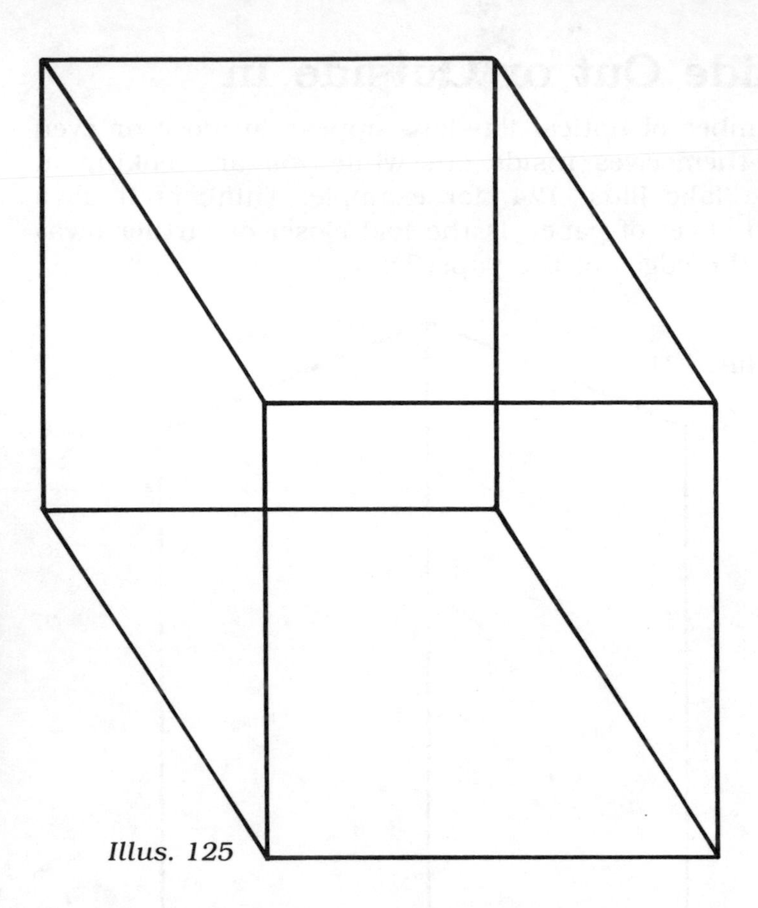

Illus. 125

How about the cube shown in Illus. 125? Are you looking at it from the front? Many people find they are looking down on it, but some think they're looking at it from underneath.

Study the cube for a few seconds. You should be able to see it move right before your eyes, just by willing yourself to see it differently.

Now what about the two squares in Illus. 126? Is the smaller, inside square closer to you than is the outside square? Or is the inside square farther away than the outside square? Study the drawing for a few seconds and once again you will find that your mind can convince you that the inside square is moving near and far.

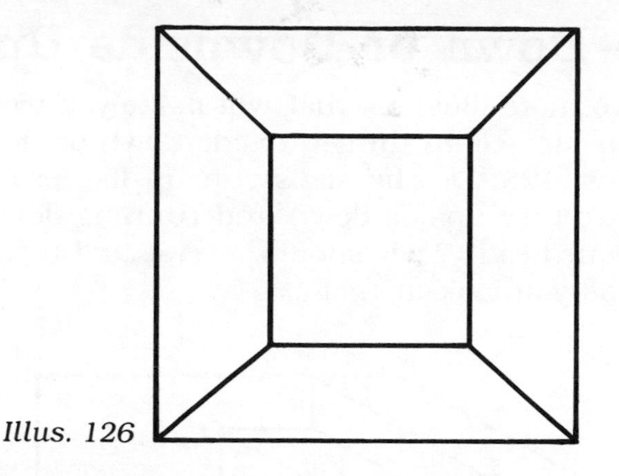

Illus. 126

Finally, check Illus. 127. Which side of the circles is open? Are you looking into the coil of circles from the right or the left? Study the drawing for a few seconds and it will move. Once you are able to see into either the right or the left side, you can make the change quickly just by telling yourself the drawing is open on the left or the right.

Illus. 127

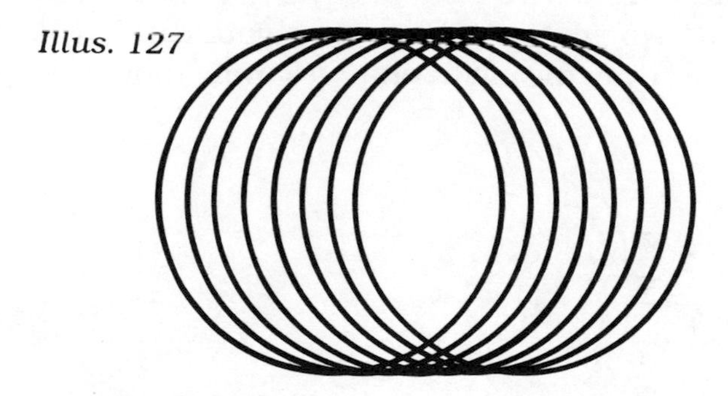

Try drawing some of these illusions on your own. Start with a drawing of an open book or the smaller square inside the larger square. Keep your drawing simple. If you draw it in just the right way, look at your drawing and you will see the drawing facing towards you or away from you. Try it and see; then experiment with other ideas of your own.

Upside Down or Downside Up

Here are two more illusions that will make you wonder whether you are seeing things upside down or not.

Check Illus. 128. Do the steps run up like ordinary steps? Or are they upside down and running downhill from over your head? They should reverse and turn upside down as you look at them.

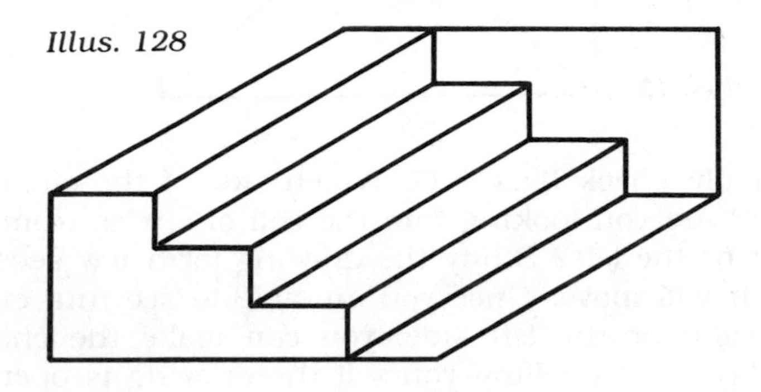

Illus. 128

Study Illus. 129. Are you looking down at it or up from below? No matter which way you think you are looking, the drawing will change and move as you study it.

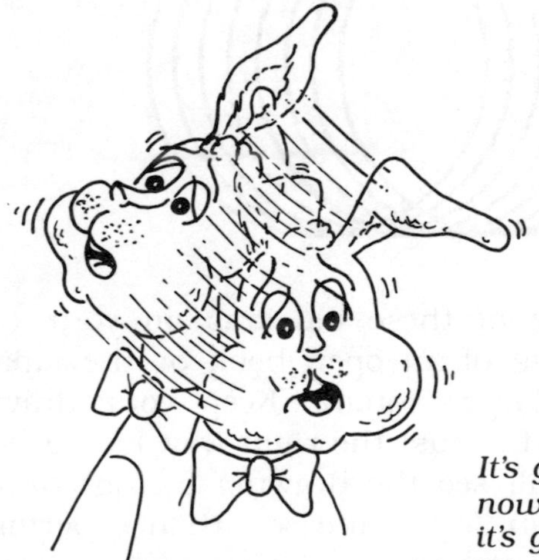

It's going up . . .
now wait a minute . . .
it's going down . . .
no . . . wait . . .

Illus. 129

• 9 •
Tricky Illusions

The Rubber Pencil

Many of the best magic tricks are really some form of moving optical illusion. Sometimes we don't see the movement, and other times we think we see something move that does not.

You may have seen a rubber pen or pencil. Some have been manufactured as jokes. However, you can make an ordinary pen or pencil appear to bend back and forth as you watch it.

Take hold of a pencil as in Illus. 130. Grip it between your thumb and finger just tightly enough so that you can flip it back and forth without it flying. Move your hand rapidly up and down as shown by the arrows in Illus. 130. Move it only a fraction of an inch. Move your hand up and down very fast.

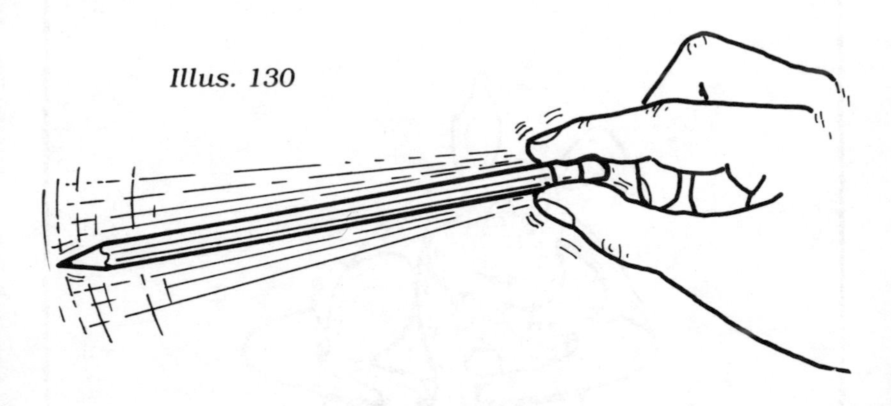

Illus. 130

You want the pencil tip to move about 3 inches up and down while the eraser end moves only ¼ an inch. Stare at the pencil an inch from the end of your thumb. As the tip moves rapidly up and down you will see the pencil seem to bend as though it were made of rubber. Practise this one until you can do it easily; then you're ready to show others your new "rubber" pencil.

The Bending Spoon

Hold a spoon in both hands as in Illus. 131. Hold it loosely so that there is room inside your cupped hand for the ends of the spoon to move around a bit.

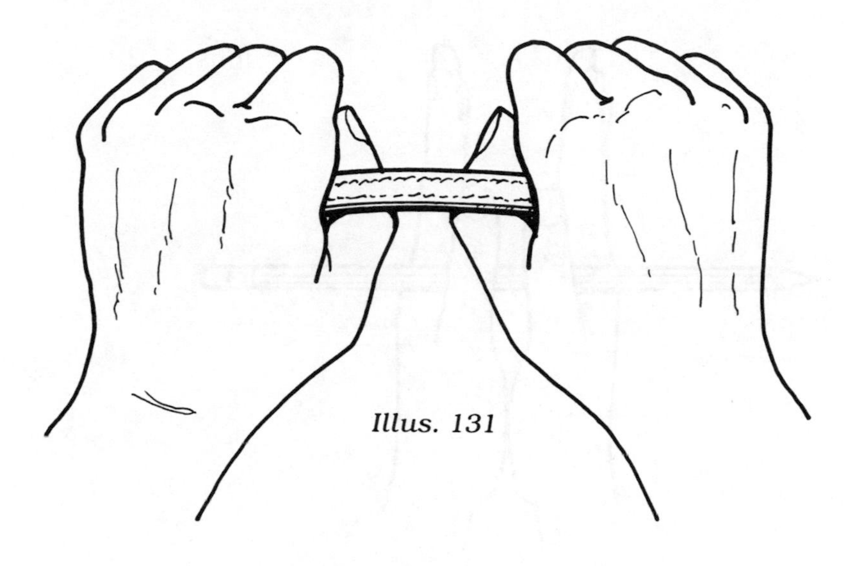

Illus. 131

Now turn the outsides of your hands downwards. The arrows in the illustration show how. But don't bend the spoon!

Let your face show that you are putting a bit of effort into bending the spoon. Of course, the ends of the spoon are slipping inside your cupped hands.

Practise this illusion in front of a mirror until you perfect it; then show others how you can bend a spoon and restore it to its original shape without so much as a tiny dent in it.

Here's a warning, however. Before someone else tries this, you'd better tip them off. You don't want to end up with a damaged spoon. Even if you didn't bend it, everyone will say it is your fault!

Reversing the Pencil

This is a very easy trick which lots of people think is an illusion. Begin by holding a long pencil as shown in Illus. 132. Slip your right thumb and left index finger over the pencil as in Illus. 133.

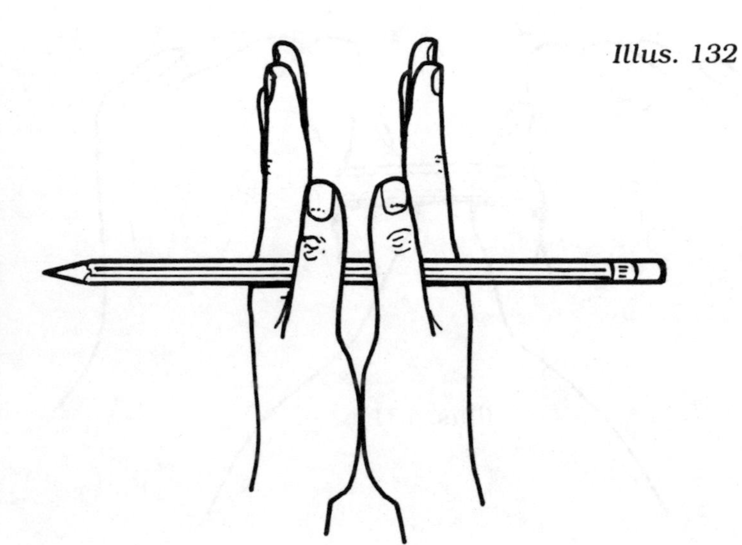

Illus. 132

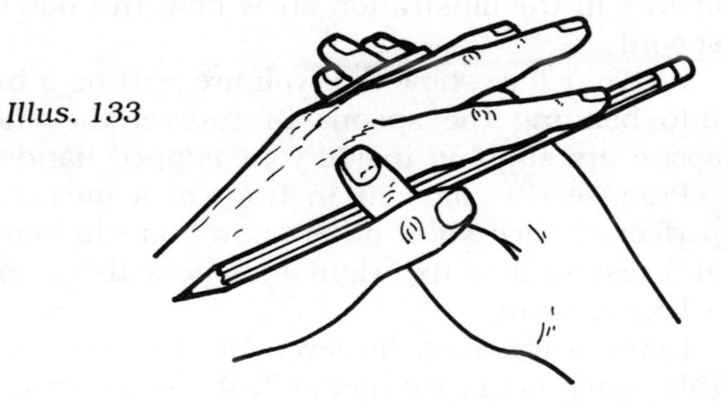

Illus. 133

Keep turning your left hand over your right so that you reach the point shown in Illus. 134. Turn both hands in towards each other and just like that the pencil will be under your hands exactly like Illus. 135.

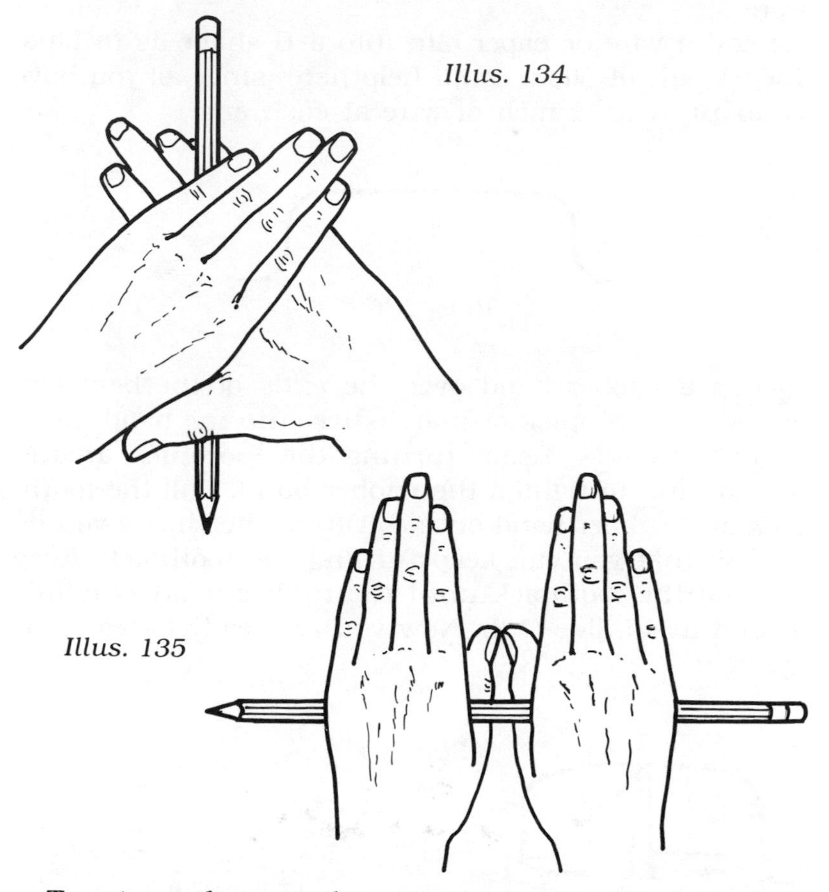

Illus. 134

Illus. 135

To return the pencil to its starting position, just reverse the steps.

This illusion takes a bit of practice. If you get stuck, start over. The main thing is to get your right thumb and left forefinger in the right place as you begin to turn the pencil.

Once you have this stunt under control, you can show it to others and let them decide if this is a real moving optical illusion.

Mind over Matter

Here's a little trick which will leave you wondering whether your eyes are as good as you thought they were.

Bend a wire or paper clip into a U shape as in Illus. 136. A pair of pliers could help here, since all you have is about ¼ to ½ inch of wire at each end.

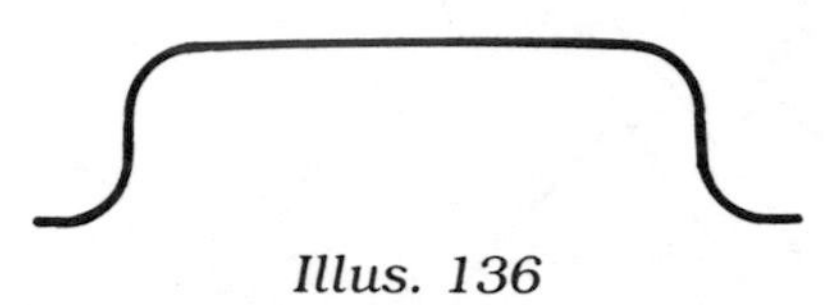

Illus. 136

Loop a rubber band over the ends of the bent clip and slip a toothpick or matchstick into the band. Illus. 137 shows how. Begin turning the toothpick around and around to tighten the rubber band. Pull the toothpick and rubber band out a bit from the clip as you do this so that you can keep turning the toothpick. Keep turning the toothpick until the rubber band is tightly wound as in Illus. 138. Now you are ready to test your eyesight.

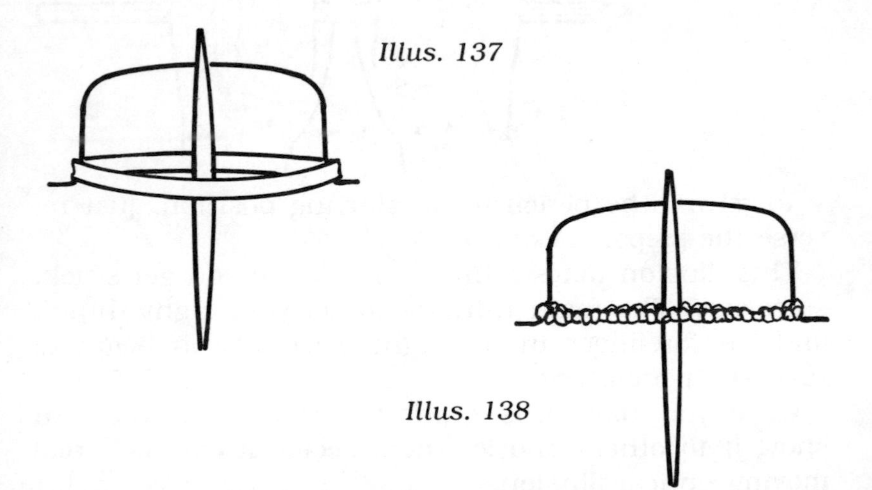

Illus. 137

Illus. 138

Hold the clip so that things look like Illus. 139. With the tip of your finger turn the toothpick one more half-turn as in Illus. 140.

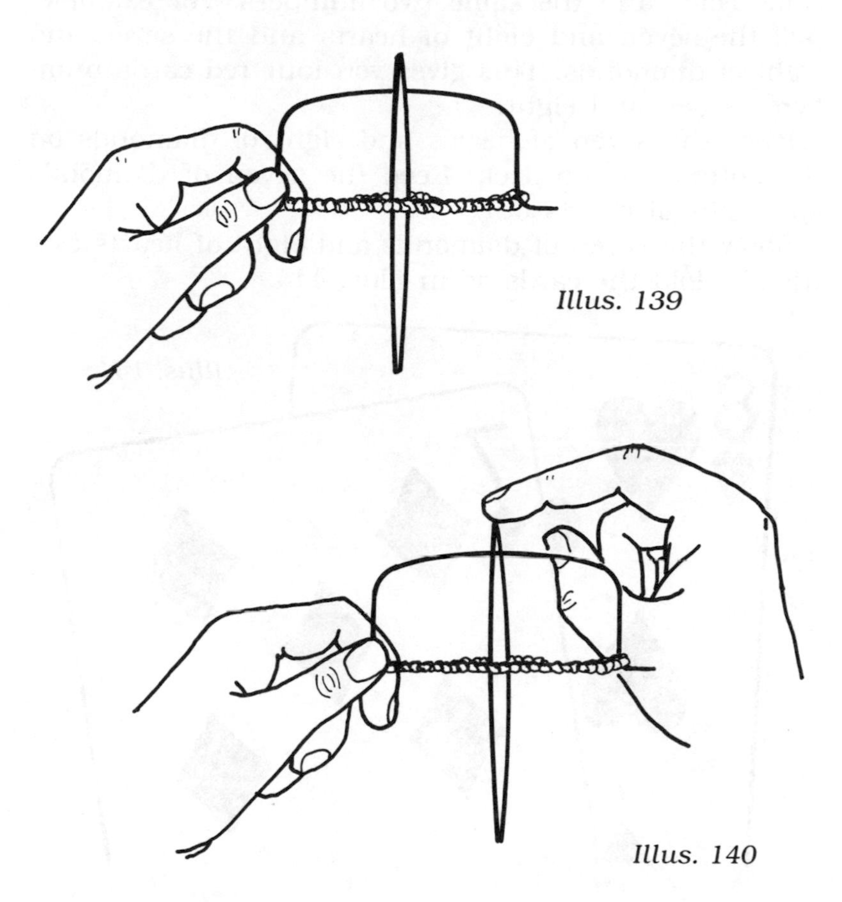

Illus. 139

Illus. 140

Let the toothpick slip off the tip of your finger. Suddenly the toothpick is back in front of the clip. Did you see it spin around? Probably not. If you did, it is because the rubber band was not wound tightly enough.

Logic says the toothpick did not come through the bent paper clip. Yet your eyes tell you they did not see the toothpick spin halfway around.

It's in the Cards

Here's a magic trick based on optical illusion.

Pull four cards from the deck. They must all be the same color and the same two numbers. For example, pull the seven and eight of hearts and the seven and eight of diamonds. This gives you four red cards numbered seven and eight.

Place the seven of hearts and eight of diamonds on the bottom of the deck. Keep the seven of diamonds and eight of hearts out.

Show the seven of diamonds and eight of hearts to a friend. Hold the cards as in Illus. 114.

Illus. 141

Now place these two cards on the top of the deck. Divide the deck in half and shuffle the halves together. Here's the time you have to be careful. Make absolutely certain the two cards you placed on the bottom stay on the bottom when you shuffle, or the trick won't work.

Be sure the two cards you put on top of the deck do not end up on top after you shuffle. Better practise this a time or two before you go public with it.

Shuffle the deck a couple of times, each time making sure the seven of hearts and the eight of diamonds are on the bottom of the deck. If this sounds complicated, it is. That's why it's a good idea to practise. Once you've done it a couple of times, you'll have no trouble at all.

Tell your audience, "Those two cards are now on the bottom of the deck." Turn the deck over and show the two red cards at the bottom as in Illus. 142.

Illus. 142

How many people realize the two cards they see are not the two they first saw? Very, very few. In fact, if you do this trick quickly and smoothly, almost no one will see that it is really an illusion.

In case anyone wants to see the top two cards, show them. They won't be the cards you put there because you shuffled.

You can do this with any cards the same color and numbers, but do it only once because you have to place the proper cards at the bottom of the deck before beginning the trick. Like all good magic based on optical illusion, you do a trick once and once only; then you find a new audience.

Index